Chemical
Dynamics

Chemical Dynamics

Joseph B. Dence
Harry B. Gray
George S. Hammond
California Institute of Technology

1968

W. A. BENJAMIN, INC.   New York   Amsterdam

CHEMICAL DYNAMICS

Copyright © 1968 by W. A. Benjamin, Inc.

Library of Congress Catalog Card Number 68–23408
Manufactured in the United States of America

*The manuscript was put into production on January 22, 1968;
this volume was published on April 22, 1968*

W. A. BENJAMIN, INC.
New York, New York 10016

Preface

CHEMICAL EDUCATION is changing rapidly, not only because of the explosive growth of knowledge but also because the new knowledge has stimulated reformulation of working principles in the science. Undergraduate curricula and individual courses are in constant flux. Nowhere is the change and challenge greater than in freshman chemistry. Teachers of freshmen must meet the intellectual needs of students who have had more sophisticated and stimulating high school courses than those given a decade ago. At the same time, the freshman teacher must be aware of the constant modification of the more advanced courses in chemistry and other fields that his students will study later.

Continuous reformulation of courses sometimes results in the inclusion of valuable new material at the expense of other equally valuable material. We believe that this has happened in some of the sophisticated courses in freshman chemistry. Structural chemistry often receives far greater emphasis than chemical dynamics. In 1965, the Westheimer Report (*Chemistry: Opportunities and Needs*, National Academy of Sciences, 1965) identified the three major fields of chemistry as *structure*, *dynamics*, and *synthesis*. We firmly believe that a balanced course in general chemistry should reflect the outlook of this report. The study of modern chemical synthesis is too demanding to be covered in depth in an introductory course. However, chemical dynamics—the systematic study of reactions and reactivity—can and should be studied at the freshman level. The study of changing chemical systems is the most fascinating part of the field for many students, and its early introduction forms a solid foundation for later study. This small volume is our attempt to answer the need.

The book is intended for students who have had introductory stoichiometry, energetics, and structure at the level of a modern freshman textbook (for example, *Basic Principles of Chemistry*, by H. B. Gray and G. P. Haight, Jr., W. A. Benjamin, Inc., New York, 1967). *Chemical Dynamics* is designed to accompany approximately 20–25 lectures to be given as the concluding section of a freshman chemistry course.

We have chosen topics for their fundamental importance in dynamics and then tried to develop a presentation suitable for freshman classes. Discussion of each topic is limited, because chemistry majors will inevitably return to all the subject matter in more advanced courses. We hope that the following ideas have been introduced with a firm conceptual basis and in enough detail for the student to apply them to chemical reality.

1. Thermodynamics and kinetics are two useful measures of reactivity.
2. Characteristic patterns of reactivity are systematically related to molecular geometry and electronic structure.
3. Reaction mechanisms are fascinating in their own right and indispensable for identification of significant problems in reaction rate theory.
4. The concepts underlying experiments with elementary reaction processes (molecular beams) are simple, even though the engineering of the experiments is complicated.
5. Application of theories of elementary reaction rates to most reactions (slow reactions, condensed media, etc.) provides enough challenge to satisfy the most ambitious young scientist.

The book includes exercises at the end of each chapter except the last. Their purpose is didactic, inasmuch as most have been written with the aim of strengthening a particular point emphasized in the chapter, or of introducing an important topic which was not developed in the text for reasons of space and which would normally be taken up in greater detail in later courses.

The material in this volume has been adapted primarily from a portion of the lectures given by H. B. G. and G. S. H. to the Chemistry 2 students at the California Institute of Technology during the academic years 1966–1967 and 1967–1968. These lectures were taped, written up by J. B. D., and distributed to the students in the form of class notes. The final manuscript was written after class-testing of the notes.

Our decision to revise the Chemistry 2 notes in the form of an introductory text was made after H. B. G. and G. S. H. participated in the San Clemente Chemical Dynamics Conference, held in December 1966 under the sponsorship of the Advisory Council of College Chemistry. At San Clemente we found we were not the only group concerned over the exclusion of significant reference to chemical reactions and reactivity relationships in freshman courses. In addition to their general encouragement, which provided the necessary additional impetus, these colleagues prepared a series of papers for publication in an issue of the *Journal of Chemical Education.* It is a pleasure to acknowledge here the direct contribution these papers made in shaping the final form of our volume; specifically, in preparing Chapter 6, we have drawn examples from the San Clemente papers of Professors R. Marcus, A. Kuppermann and E. F. Greene, and J. Halpern.

The concluding chapter of this book was developed from the lectures given by Professors E. F. Greene (dynamics in simple systems), Richard Wolfgang (atomic carbon), John D. Roberts (nuclear magnetic resonance), and F. C. Anson (electrochemical dynamics) to the students of Chemistry 2 in May 1967. These colleagues have kindly given us permission to use their material.

We are grateful to Professors Ralph G. Pearson and Paul Haake, who read the entire manuscript and offered valuable criticism. It is a special pleasure to acknowledge the enormous contribution our students in Chemistry 2 made to the project. Their enthusiastic, critical attitude helped us make many improvements in the manuscript. Thanks are also due to four very special members of the staff of W. A. Benjamin, Inc., for seeing this project through with infectious vigor. Finally, and not the least, we acknowledge the role Susan Brittenham and Eileen McKoy played in preparing the final manuscript.

JOSEPH B. DENCE
HARRY B. GRAY
GEORGE S. HAMMOND

Pasadena, California
January 1968

Contents

Preface   **v**

1 Chemical Energetics   **1**
   1-1 Introduction   1
   1-2 Chemical Potential and Equilibrium   2
      Exercises   5

**2 Application of the Chemical Potential to Acid
Ionization**   **7**
   2-1 Ionization Equilibria   7
   2-2 Correlation with Gross Structure   9
      Exercises   14

**3 Energetics of Acid Ionization in the Born–Haber
Cycle**   **17**
   3-1 Introduction   17
   3-2 The Born–Haber Cycle   18
   3-3 Evaluation of the Born–Haber Terms   20
      Exercises   28

**4 Energetics of Acid Ionization in a Cycle Including
Electroreduction Potentials**   **30**

4–1   Introduction   30
4–2   Measurement of Reduction Potentials   34
4–3   Analysis of Data   36
      Exercises   38

5   **Rate Phenomena in Chemical Reactivity**   41
5–1   Introduction   41
5–2   Reaction Mechanisms   43
5–3   Elementary Reactions   43
      Exercises   44

6   **Elementary Reaction Processes in Gaseous
    and Liquid Systems**   45
6–1   Recent Experimental and Theoretical Advances   45
6–2   Reactions in the Gaseous Phase   47
6–3   Reactions in Liquid Solutions   56
      Exercises   62

7   **An Illustrative Chemical Reaction**   65
7–1   The Iodide-Hypochlorite Reaction   65
7–2   Interpretation of the Rate Constant   67
      Exercises   69

8   **Mechanisms and Rate Laws**   71
8–1   The Rate-Determining Step   71
8–2   An Alternative Mechanism   72
8–3   A Further Look at the First Mechanism   73
      Exercises   75

9   **The Interpretation of Rate Equations by Means
    of the Collision and the Transition State Theories** 77
9–1   The Collision Theory   77
9–2   The Transition State Theory   80
      Exercises   82

Contents [xi]

10 Classification of Reactions, Reactants, and
    Mechanisms   85
    10-1 Types of Reactions   85
    10-2 Types of Reactants   88
    10-3 Types of Mechanisms   89
    10-4 Summary   91
          Exercises   92

11 Reaction Chemistry of Compounds of the
    Second-Row Elements with Emphasis on Boron   95
    11-1 An Outline of Reactions of Compounds of
          Second-Row Elements   95
    11-2 Mechanisms for Boron Chemistry   97
          Exercises   101

12 Reaction Chemistry of Compounds of Carbon,
    Nitrogen, Oxygen, and Fluorine   103
    12-1 Mechanisms for Carbon   103
    12-2 Mechanisms for Nitrogen   106
    12-3 Mechanisms for Oxygen and Fluorine   111
          Exercises   113

13 Reactivity Correlations   117
    13-1 The Nature of Correlations   117
    13-2 Specific Examples of Correlation: The
          Swain–Scott and Edwards Equations   119
    13-3 Importance of the Nature of the Substrate   122
    13-4 The Concept of Hard and Soft Acids and Bases   126
          Exercises   128

14 Substitution Reactions of Complexes of Metal Ions   133
    14-1 Introduction   133
    14-2 Overall Look at Metal Ion Rates   134
    14-3 A Closer Look at the Energetics Involved in
          Dissociative and Associative Mechanisms   136

14–4   Ligand Substitution Dynamics in
         Square-Planar Complexes   139
14–5   Ligand Substitution Dynamics in Octahedral
         Complexes   147
         Exercises   151

15   Lectures on Frontier Areas in Chemical Dynamics   153
15–1   Chemical Dynamics in Really Simple Systems   154
15–2   Reactions of Atomic Carbon   161
15–3   Chemical Dynamics as Revealed by Nuclear
         Magnetic Resonance Spectroscopy   166
15–4   Electrochemical Dynamics   173

Index   181

I

Chemical Energetics

1-1 INTRODUCTION

Chemical dynamics encompasses the study of chemical reactions and reactivity. A knowledge of how complex chemical processes take place is among the most important goals of contemporary science. Ultimately, detailed understanding of molecular transformations will allow man to synthesize materials of super strength or other desired properties, produce energy efficiently and cleanly to drive machines, and even control life itself.

Scientists have not yet advanced the study of chemical dynamics to the point where we can describe in fullest detail the process of molecular transformation. However, it is possible to analyze a large body of experimental data on the energetics and rates of chemical reactions. Our purpose in this introductory text is to present the energetics, the rates, and the probable reaction pathways for a number of representative chemical transformations. We shall interpret these results in terms of modern theory. In the final chapter there is presented material summarized from four of the most recent and active areas of research in chemical dynamics. Throughout, we shall assume that the reader has had an introduction to the electronic structures of chemical systems.[1]

---

[1] The level of our presentation assumes coverage of the type given in H. B. Gray and G. P. Haight, Jr., *Basic Principles of Chemistry*, particularly Chapters 8, 9, 11, 12, 13, and 16, W. A. Benjamin, Inc., New York, 1967.

[1]

1-2   CHEMICAL POTENTIAL AND
EQUILIBRIUM

Chemical energetics provides a convenient and elegant language for discussion of problems in chemical dynamics. We should ask ourselves questions such as: how much energy is required to form a mole of compound A, how much heat is given off when B is completely converted to C, or, is it feasible to expect compound F to be formed from D via E as an intermediate? In order to talk intelligently about chemical energetics, it is necessary to establish a language for communication. The language used universally is the language of thermodynamics, although it should be pointed out that many other scientific disciplines besides chemistry make extensive use of thermodynamics.

A thorough digression into the fundamentals of chemical thermodynamics is not practical at this point. It is assumed that the student is familiar with the basic concepts of work and energy, and with some of the thermodynamic functions such as heat capacity, enthalpy, and free energy.[2]

The idea that chemical reactions occur because there is some kind of driving force behind them is well known. If the reaction occurs at constant pressure[3] this driving force is called the free energy change and may be illustrated by the following example. Consider the reversible dissociation of gaseous phosphorus pentachloride into phosphorus trichloride and chlorine,

$$PCl_5 \rightleftharpoons PCl_3 + Cl_2$$

and let us further suppose that the reaction is carried out at constant volume and at a constant temperature T. At time $t = 0$, the system consists only of phosphorus pentachloride or of phosphorus trichloride plus chlorine, but we would like to characterize the system

---

[2] If this is not the case, excellent coverage can be found in J. Waser, *Basic Chemical Thermodynamics*, W. A. Benjamin, Inc., New York, 1966.

[3] The value of free energy as a measure of driving force stems from the fact that many reactions are carried out under the nearly constant pressure of 1 atm.

at some later time $t > 0$. The system will then have a tendency to proceed in one direction or the other; the quantitative measure of this tendency is the free energy change (ΔG) which is expressed as follows:

$$\Delta G = \Delta H - T\,\Delta S = \Delta \tilde{G}^{\circ}(T) + 2.303RT \log \frac{[P_{\mathrm{PCl_3}}]_t[P_{\mathrm{Cl_2}}]_t}{[P_{\mathrm{PCl_5}}]_t} \qquad (1\text{-}1)$$

where ΔH and ΔS are the changes in enthalpy and entropy, $\Delta \tilde{G}^{\circ}(T)$ is the change in free energy accompanying the conversion of 1 mole of phosphorus pentachloride, at 1 atm pressure, to 1 mole of phosphorus trichloride and 1 mole of chlorine, both at 1 atm pressure with the transformation occurring at the absolute temperature T. The values of ΔG, ΔH, and ΔS, on the other hand, are the changes in the thermodynamic functions at the reaction (pressure) conditions, that is, using the pressures of the reactants and products that are involved in the particular experiment. By convention, if $\Delta G < 0$, then the reaction will proceed to the right spontaneously, while if $\Delta G > 0$, the reaction tends to proceed to the left spontaneously.

An important case occurs when $\Delta G = 0$. Under these conditions, the tendency to proceed in either direction is the same; we say that the system has reached equilibrium. Equation (1-1) can then be written as

$$\Delta \tilde{G}^{\circ}(T) = -2.303RT \log \frac{[P_{\mathrm{PCl_3}}]_{eq}[P_{\mathrm{Cl_2}}]_{eq}}{[P_{\mathrm{PCl_5}}]_{eq}} \qquad (1\text{-}2)$$

or, by defining the equilibrium pressure quotient as the *equilibrium constant* for the reaction, this finally becomes

$$\Delta^{\circ}\tilde{G}(T) = -2.303RT \log K_{eq} \qquad (1\text{-}3)$$

Another way of saying that $\Delta G = 0$ is that the sum of the free energies of the products equals that for the reactants:

$$(G_{\mathrm{PCl_3}})_{eq} + (G_{\mathrm{Cl_2}})_{eq} = (G_{\mathrm{PCl_5}})_{eq} \qquad (1\text{-}4)$$

This simple statement corresponds nicely to our physical intuition which suggests that when a system is at equilibrium something is being balanced. Of course, we could say that there is a balance between the forward rate of dissociation and the reverse rate of association. This is true, but in order to make such a statement we are required to know something about the details of how the reaction occurs.

Another important point is that the quantities in Equation (1–4) are *extensive* quantities, that is, they depend on the amount of material present. It would be more convenient, however, to have available an *intensive* quantity which can be used in formulating criteria for equilibrium. If we have a mixture of n_1 moles of species 1, n_2 moles of species 2, and so on, then the *chemical potential* μ_k has the properties that $n_k\mu_k = n_k\tilde{G}_k = G_k$, where $\tilde{G}_k$ is the partial molar free energy of species k. The *total* free energy of the mixture then is the sum of the free energies of the constituents:

$$G_{\mathrm{mix}} = \sum_i n_i\mu_i \qquad (1\text{–}5)$$

When considering infinitesimal changes in the composition of a system, it is necessary that the chemical potential be formulated in terms of the language of partial derivatives; the treatment in this book will be of an introductory nature and will not involve partial derivatives.

The chemical potential is quite analogous to other potential quantities such as potential energy and electrical potential. For chemical purposes, the significance of μ is that the chemical potential of a pure compound or of a component of a mixture can be thought of as a measure of the potential for getting work from the system if we are willing to change the number of moles of that substance. The condition for equilibrium at some temperature T for the system

$$a\mathrm{A} + b\mathrm{B} \rightleftharpoons c\mathrm{C} + d\mathrm{D}$$

can now be formulated as

$$a\mu_\mathrm{A} + b\mu_\mathrm{B} = c\mu_\mathrm{C} + d\mu_\mathrm{D} \qquad (1\text{–}6)$$

From Equation (1–6) one can deduce for example that if a single material is distributed between two phases (either of itself or of another material), say gaseous and liquid, then the condition for equilibrium is that

$$\mu(g) = \mu(l) \qquad (1\text{–}7)$$

The exact form in which μ is written depends on whether the material is in a solid, liquid, or gaseous phase. Equation (1–7) further

TABLE 1-1
Expressions for the Chemical Potential

State	Expression	Standard state
Component of a mixture of ideal gases	$\mu_i = \mu_i^\circ + 2.303RT \log P_i$	Partial pressure 1 atm, temperature T, $\mu_i^\circ (T)$ $= \bar{G}_i^\circ(T)$
Molecular component of an ideal solution	$\mu_i = \mu_i^\circ + 2.303RT \log[c_i]$	Temperature T and concentration $1M$
Ionic component of an ideal solution	$\mu_i = \mu_i^\circ + 2.303RT \log[c_i]_{\text{ion}}$	Temperature T, concentration $1M$, and $\mu_i^\circ(H^+) = 0$

suggests that μ is to be defined relative to some particular reference state. Table 1-1 summarizes some useful forms for the chemical potential.

Appropriate modifications of these expressions must be made if we are not dealing with ideal gases or solutions. It should also be noted that even though these expressions appear to require us to take the logarithm of a quantity possessing units, this is not actually the case since the logarithmic terms involve ratios of the pressures or concentrations to those in the standard states, for example, $\log P_i/P_0$. A quantity such as P_i/P_0 becomes equal to the numerical value of P_i with no units, because standard pressures or concentrations are unity.

EXERCISES

1. Consider the reaction $2HI(g) \rightleftharpoons H_2(g) + I_2(g)$, in which, at 25°C, the hydrogen iodide is 16.3% dissociated. Suppose at time $t = 0$ an evacuated 1-liter container is charged with 1 mole each of hydrogen and hydrogen

iodide and the system brought to equilibrium by means of a suitable catalyst. Assume all components behave as ideal gases.

(a) What will the final total pressure be?

(b) What is $\Delta \tilde{G}°$ for the process at 25°C?

2. Write expressions for the equilibrium constants of the following reactions:

(a) $Ca(s) + CO_2(g) \rightleftharpoons CaO(s) + CO(g)$

(b) $H_2O(l) \rightleftharpoons H_2O(g)$

(c) $4 Br^-(aq) + O_2(g) + 4H^+(aq) \rightleftharpoons 2H_2O(l) + 2Br_2(g)$

(d) $H_3PO_4(aq) + H_2O(l) \rightleftharpoons H_3O^+(aq) + H_2PO_4^-(aq)$

3. Classify the following as extensive or intensive properties: molar volume, temperature, pressure, density, total energy, index of refraction, mole fraction.

4. Absent from Table 1–1 is the expression for the chemical potential of a pure liquid. What form do you suppose it has?

5. Use Table 1–1 to express the condition for equilibrium in terms of chemical potentials for gaseous hydrogen chloride which is in equilibrium with an aqueous solution.

6. The triple point of benzene, at which solid, liquid, and vapor coexist, occurs at 5.3°C. What can you infer about the standard free energies of solid and liquid benzene at this temperature?

II

Application of the Chemical Potential to Acid Ionization

2-1 IONIZATION EQUILIBRIA

We shall commence discussion of the systematics in the variation of chemical reactivity of substances in solution by considering the ionization of protonic acids. A sufficient supply of relevant data is available because chemists have recognized for a long time the importance of acids and bases. Much of the data relate to ionization in the solvent water, since this is the most available common solvent.

Consider now an acid HA dissolved in water. Its ionization can be written as follows:

$$H_2O(l) + HA(aq) \rightleftharpoons H_3O^+(aq) + A^-(aq)$$

Notice that this formulation explicitly includes water as a participant in the reaction; chemists believe that even this is a simplification of the true state of affairs. More complex aggregates, such as $H_5O_2^+$, are thought to exist and the anion A^- is also solvated. We shall not concern ourselves with these structural details. Thermodynamically, the ionization reaction, at equilibrium, can be put into the following language:

$$\mu_{H_2O(l)} + \mu_{HA(aq)} = \mu_{H_3O^+(aq)} + \mu_{A^-(aq)} \tag{2-1}$$

[7]

or by using the definition of chemical potential for each of these species,

$$\mu°_{H_2O(l)} + 2.303RT \log[H_2O] + \mu°_{HA(aq)} + 2.303RT \log[HA]$$
$$= \mu°_{H_3O^+(aq)} + 2.303RT \log[H_3O^+] + \mu°_{A^-(aq)}$$
$$+ 2.303RT \log[A^-] \qquad (2\text{-}2)$$

Two slight modifications of this equation can be introduced at this point. First, for all but the most dilute solutions, the behavior of the solute cannot be expected to approximate ideality. It becomes necessary to substitute for concentrations quantities called *activities*, which are defined as

$$a_i = c_i\gamma_i \qquad (2\text{-}3)$$

where γ_i is the activity coefficient and is in essence a measure of the nonideality of the ith species. It should be pointed out, however, that modern solution theory has not yet reached a point where activity coefficients can be accurately calculated for solutions of concentrations much above 0.01 molar; therefore, Equation (2-3) is only an operational definition of the activity of a species.

Second, since water is the solvent, its activity is approximately that of the pure liquid, which is unity by convention. Equation (2-2) can thus be rewritten as

$$\tilde{G}°_{H_2O(l)} + \tilde{G}°_{HA(aq)} + 2.303RT \log a_{HA(aq)} = \tilde{G}°_{H_3O^+(aq)}$$
$$+ 2.303RT \log a_{H_3O^+(aq)} + \tilde{G}°_{A^-(aq)} + 2.303RT \log a_{A^-(aq)} \quad (2\text{-}4)$$

Combining the molar free energies leads to the more compact expression

$$\Delta\tilde{G}° = -2.303RT \log \frac{a_{H_3O^+(aq)}a_{A^-(aq)}}{a_{HA(aq)}} \qquad (2\text{-}5)$$

Only in cases where the ratio of the activity coefficients in the logarithmic term is nearly unity is it acceptable to use concentrations instead of activities.

Data for acid ionization are often presented not as values for $\Delta\tilde{G}°$, but rather in terms of a quantity known as the pK, which is defined as follows:

$$pK = -\log K_i \qquad (2\text{-}6)$$

This quantity is very attractive to deal with because it is proportional to the free energy of dissociation. Utilizing the fact that $\Delta \tilde{G}^\circ = -2.303RT \log K_i$, we see that (2–6) is equivalent to

$$pK = \frac{\Delta \tilde{G}^\circ}{2.303RT} \tag{2-7}$$

At 25°C the term $2.303RT$ has the value 1.37 kcal, so that the magnitudes of the $\Delta \tilde{G}^\circ$ values are approximately equal to those of the pK values.

Notice that as the pK increases, the acid becomes weaker, that is, more free energy is required to ionize it. Combining Equations (2–5) and (2–6) yields another interesting property of the pK

$$pK = pH - \log \left[\frac{a_{A^-(aq)}}{a_{HA(aq)}} \right] \tag{2-8}$$

This follows from the rigorous definition of the pH. However, since it does not appear possible *experimentally* to measure activity coefficients for single ions (that is, for sodium ions in aqueous solution in the absence of anion), it is more practical to assume $a_{H^+(aq)} \approx [H^+]$, and to rewrite (2–8) as

$$pK = pH - \log \frac{[A^-]}{[HA]} \tag{2-9}$$

To a first approximation, (2–9) tells us that if we carry out a titration and stop at the point where $[A^-] = [HA]$, then the pH of the solution will be equal to the pK of the acid. This directly gives a good method for estimating the ionization constant of the acid.

2-2 CORRELATION WITH GROSS STRUCTURE

It is now useful to discuss the kinds of correlation which can be made between acidity constant and structure of the acid. Consider the ionization of two weak acids:

$$HA(aq) \overset{K_1}{\rightleftharpoons} H^+(aq) + A^-(aq)$$
$$HB(aq) \overset{K_2}{\rightleftharpoons} H^+(aq) + B^-(aq)$$

We would like to understand why K_1 and K_2 are different, if they are,

and why they are different by as much as they are, or why they are
the same if this is the case. The reason for doing this is that by
examination of a mass of available data, one may hope to lay down
some guidelines governing the correlation between acidity constant
and structure and then go on to predict the acidity constant K_3 of
some different acid. More importantly, if these correlations prove to
be fruitful, it may be possible to transfer the techniques used and
perhaps some of the quantitative information to the solving of many
other reactivity problems.

A useful way of looking at the comparison of two weak acids is to
study the proton-exchange reaction

$$HA(aq) + B^-(aq) \overset{K}{\rightleftharpoons} A^-(aq) + HB(aq)$$

where $K = K_1/K_2$. This latter relation is easily seen by noting that

$$\Delta \tilde{G}^\circ = -2.303RT \left[\log \frac{a_{H^+(aq)} a_{A^-(aq)}}{a_{HA(aq)}} - \log \frac{a_{H^+(aq)} a_{B^-(aq)}}{a_{HB(aq)}} \right] \quad (2\text{--}10)$$

In many cases K can be measured directly, and we see that by comparing the two acids directly we eliminate the need of knowing the
activity coefficient of the hydrogen ion.

Let us now look at the acidity constants for some acids derived
from elements in the second row of the periodic table.

These data display a large spread in values for the acidity constant.
In terms of energy differences, however, the spread does not seem so
large. Consider the following proton-transfer reaction:

$$NH_2^-(aq) + HF(aq) \rightleftharpoons NH_3(aq) + F^-(aq)$$

The equilibrium constant for this reaction has the magnitude of 10^{19},

TABLE 2-1

**Ionization Data for Some Second-Row Acids
in Water at 25°C**

Acid		pK
Hydrofluoric acid	F—H	3
Water	HO—H	14
Ammonia	H₂N—H	22

and therefore from Equation (2–7) the change in standard free energy $\Delta \tilde{G}^\circ$ is approximately $1.37 \times 19 = 26$ kcal mole^{-1}. In contrast, most bond-breaking processes occur with free energy changes of 60–105 kcal mole^{-1}. Even though chemically the acids in Table 2–1 are quite different as far as their reactivity is concerned, we see that this is a consequence of a relatively modest difference in standard free energies of ionization. Correspondingly, this tells us that small energy differences, perhaps on the order of just a few kilocalories per mole, can result in very important differences in chemical reactivity.

Table 2–2 shows more data on the acidity constants of various acids. From an examination of the pK values of sulfuric and sulfurous acids, selenic and selenous acids, and *many other such pairs*, one is led to conclude that the weaker acid contains a smaller number of X=O groups. The pK of telluric acid, however, is some 3.7 pK units greater than that for tellurous acid. This anomaly was puzzling until other methods of study indicated that the structure of telluric acid in water solution is not $(HO)_2TeO_2$, but is more properly written as $(HO)_6Te$, the product of addition of two molecules of water to the simpler species.

$$(HO)_2TeO_2 + 2H_2O \overset{K}{\rightleftharpoons} Te(OH)_6 \qquad K \gg 1$$

'TABLE 2–2

Ionization Data for Various Inorganic Acids in Water at 25°C

Acid		pK	Structure
Sulfuric acid	H_2SO_4	-3	$(HO)_2SO_2$
Sulfurous acid	H_2SO_3	1.8	$(HO)_2SO$
Selenic acid	H_2SeO_4	-3	$(HO)_2SeO_2$
Selenous acid	H_2SeO_3	2.5	$(HO)_2SeO$
Telluric acid	H_6TeO_6	6.2	$(HO)_6Te$
Tellurous acid	H_2TeO_3	2.5	$(HO)_2TeO$
Phosphoric acid	H_3PO_4	2.1	$(HO)_3PO$
Dihydrogen phosphate ion	$H_2PO_4^-$	6.9	$(HO)_2PO_2^-$
Phosphorous acid	H_3PO_3	1.2	$(HO)_2(H)PO$
Dihydrogen phosphite ion	$H_2PO_3^-$	4.7	$(HO)(H)PO_2^-$
Hypophosphorous acid	H_3PO_2	1.5	$(HO)(H)_2PO$

This difference in structure from sulfuric and selenic acids is responsible for the anomalous change in the variation of pK values.

Examination of some acids of phosphorus reveals another apparent anomaly. Phosphorous and hypophosphorous acids might be expected to be considerably weaker than phosphoric acid, whereas in fact all three acids are of comparable strength. Once again, reactivity considerations led to a reinvestigation of the structures of the two acids and it has now been shown that, in contrast to phosphoric acid, the other two acids have the structures shown below.

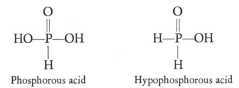

| Phosphorous acid | Hypophosphorous acid |

Another interesting series which has been extensively studied consists of various aliphatic carboxylic acids. In Table 2–3 are presented the data for a limited number of derivatives of acetic acid.

One can see that fluorine and chlorine act in the same direction in influencing acid strength. Furthermore, it appears that successive substitution results in a monotonic variation in the acidity constant. The difference in pK values between the strongest and the weakest acids, 4.15 pK units, amounts to a standard free energy difference of only $1.37 \times 4.15 = 5.7$ kcal mole^{-1}. In many instances, interpretation of such a small energy difference would be very risky, but under

TABLE 2–3

**Ionization Data for Acetic Acids
in Water at 25°C**

Acid		pK
Acetic acid	CH_3COOH	4.80
Fluoroacetic acid	$F—CH_2COOH$	2.86
Chloroacetic acid	$Cl—CH_2COOH$	2.66
Dichloroacetic acid	$Cl_2CH\ COOH$	1.30
Trichloroacetic acid	Cl_3CCOOH	0.65

the conditions of a carefully controlled set of small systematic changes, a difference of 5 kcal mole^{-1} may be rationalized.

This point is even more strikingly illustrated by examining a series of substituted benzoic acids. These acids have been most extensively

TABLE 2-4

Ionization Data for Ionization of Substituted Benzoic Acids in Water at 25°C^a

Acid		*p*K
m-Toluic	CH$_3$ / COOH	4.27
Benzoic acid	COOH	4.20
m-Methoxybenzoic acid	OCH$_3$ / COOH	4.09
m-Fluorobenzoic acid	F / COOH	3.87
m-Chlorobenzoic acid	Cl / COOH	3.82
m-Bromobenzoic acid	Br / COOH	3.81
m-Nitrobenzoic acid	NO$_2$ / COOH	3.49
m-Diazobenzoic acid	N$_2$$^+$ / COOH	2.44

^{a} The 1.83 unit spread in pK values is equivalent to a standard free energy difference of only 2.5 kcal mole^{-1}, yet the difference in chemical reactivities between the strongest and the weakest acids is easily interpretable in the same way as in the acetic acids considered earlier.

TABLE 2–5

Ionization Data for Hydrohalic
Acids in Water at 25°C

Acid	pK
Hydrofluoric acid	3
Hydrochloric acid	-9^a
Hydrobromic acid	-11^a
Hydriodic acid	-10^a

[a] Estimated values; see Chapter 4.

studied by numerous workers, and some relevant data are given in Table 2–4.

We now want to look more closely at the problem of explaining the variation of acidity constants in some series of acids in terms of systematic structural changes.   Let us consider the set of hydrohalic acids given in Table 2–5.   We should like to understand in more detail what energy terms are responsible for the great difference in acid strength between HF and the heavier HX acids.   We can hope that a close examination of a series such as this one might provide some guidance in correlating chemical reactivities in other series. This problem will form the subject of our next two chapters.

EXERCISES

1. Derive a simple relationship between pH and the chemical potential $\mu_{H^+(aq)}$ of hydrogen ions in aqueous solution.

2. Several years ago Linus Pauling pointed out that the ratio K_1/K_2 for several dibasic oxyacids (such as carbonic acid and $H_2PO_4^-$) is approximately 10^5.

$$H_2A(aq) \overset{K_1}{\rightleftharpoons} H^+(aq) + HA^-(aq)$$

$$HA^-(aq) \overset{K_2}{\rightleftharpoons} H^+(aq) + A^-(aq)$$

To what free energy difference ($\Delta \tilde{G}^\circ$) does this correspond? It is interesting to examine the magnitude of K_1/K_2 for a series of acids as the two ionizable protons are situated farther and farther apart. For H_2S the ratio is 4.8×10^7, for H_2CO_3 it is 7.7×10^5, and for succinic acid $HOOC—(CH_2)_2—COOH$ it is 27. In the limit of very distantly separated protons, what value do you think the ratio K_1/K_2 approaches?

3. To 30 ml of 0.01 molar Na_2CO_3 a student adds 25 ml of 0.018 molar HCl. Measurement of the pH of the solution with a pH meter gives a value of 6.41. What can he infer from these data?

4. From the data of Tables 2–1 and 2–5 predict which acid in the following pairs is the stronger:

$$H_2S \text{ or } H_2O$$
$$PH_3 \text{ or } NH_3$$
$$HCl \text{ or } H_2S$$

5. (a) Predict the direction of these reactions from qualitative considerations:

$$HS^-(aq) + H_3PO_4(aq) \rightleftharpoons H_2S(aq) + H_2PO_4^-(aq)$$
$$NH_3(aq) + OH^-(aq) \rightleftharpoons NH_2^-(aq) + H_2O$$
$$HTeO_3^-(aq) + HF(aq) \rightleftharpoons H_2TeO_3(aq) + F^-(aq)$$

(b) Check these predictions by calculation of $\Delta \tilde{G}^\circ$ values in each case.

6. A 0.0078 molar aqueous solution of acetic acid is 4.8% dissociated. Assuming that the activity coefficient of the acetic acid is 1.0, estimate the value of the product $\gamma_{H_3O^+(aq)} \, \gamma_{A^-(aq)}$ for this solution. Would you say that the solution can be reasonably approximated as an ideal solution? Note again that the activity-coefficient product cannot be dissected into its constituent parts.

7. The reactions of a large number of benzene derivatives can be successfully correlated by means of the equation

$$\log \left(\frac{K}{K_0} \right) = \rho \sigma$$

In this expression K is the equilibrium constant for the substituted benzene under study, K_0 is the constant for the reference (or unsubstituted) material in the series, ρ is a constant characteristic of the particular class of reaction under consideration, and σ is a constant characteristic of the particular substituent.

(a) In Table 2–6 is given a list of σ constants. Convince yourself that the data of Table 2–4 do indeed follow the equation $\log (K/K_0) = \rho \sigma$. What is your value of ρ for the ionization of benzoic acids in water at 25°C?

(b) What must logically be the value of σ for the protonic substituent?

TABLE 2–6

σ-Parameters for *m*-Benzoic Acids

Substituent	σ
CH_3O	0.115
CH_3	−0.069
F	0.337
Cl	0.373
Br	0.391
I	0.352
NO_2	0.710
N_2^+	1.76
$C_6H_5 - I^+$	1.00

(c) Is the relative order of effects due to fluorine and chlorine substituents retained for both acetic and benzoic acid systems?

(d) Give a qualitative, electronic structural rationalization of the large σ differences displayed in Table 2–6.

(e) Estimate the pK of *m*-iodobenzoic acid and compare with the *m*-fluoro, *m*-chloro, and *m*-bromo acids. What can you infer from this?

(f) For the ionization of cinnamic acids in water at 25°C the value of ρ is 0.466. Predict the dissociation constant of the substituted cinnamic acid below.

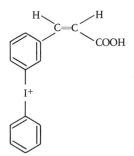

III

Energetics of Acid Ionization in the Born–Haber Cycle

3-1 INTRODUCTION

If any real value is to be derived from discussion of the relationship between structure and reactivity, we must be able to predict further results in advance of experiment. Two kinds of predictions are common. First, we may predict the change in reactivity in a particular reaction that may result from a particular change in structure. For example, if we know that fluoroacetic acid is a stronger acid than acetic acid, we will without much hesitation predict that chloroacetic acid will also be stronger than acetic acid (p. 12). With experience we may even make a quantitative prediction. The second kind of prediction involves prediction of reactivity relationships in a new reaction. Consider the following reactions:

$$XCH_2COOH \rightleftharpoons XCH_2COO^- + H^+$$
$$XCH_2COOAg(s) \rightleftharpoons XCH_2COO^- + Ag^+$$

We can expect that there will be some kind of systematic relationship between the acidity constants of derivatives of acetic acid and the solubilities of the silver salts of the acids. Since the different silver salts may be packed differently in their crystal lattices, the relationship will not necessarily be simple. In fact, it may turn

[17]

out that comparison of solubility data will provide a way of looking for interesting variations in the crystal structure of the silver salts. We do not propose to analyze the problem, but suggest it as an example of what we might try to do in correlating reactivity relationships in two different reactions.

We have considerable faith that such correlations of the behavior of sets of compounds in different reactions must exist, as an expression of the fundamental regularity of physical phenomena. Sometimes valuable correlations are discovered purely empirically. In other cases, correlations which are intuitively expected are established as valid only by very careful analysis of the relationships between reactions. Consider the comparison of the ionization of hydrogen halides in water solution (p. 14) and the dissociation of the halides in the gaseous state to give atoms.

Ionization in water solution:
$$HX(aq) \rightleftharpoons H^+(aq) + X^-(aq)$$
Dissociation to atoms in gaseous state:
$$HX(g) \rightleftharpoons H \cdot (g) + X \cdot (g)$$

Since both reactions involve breaking of H—X bonds the energetics of the two processes should be related. However, one process leads to ions in water solution and the other leads to atoms in the gas phase; the relationships can often be carried out by formulating thermodynamic cycles, in which molecules are taken through a series of imagined experiments, so that a chemical change can be accomplished by two different routes. Since the overall change in the free energy (or entropy or enthalpy) must be the same for both paths, consideration of the steps in the cycle allows us to use data obtained from various sources to establish the desired reactivity relationships. In this chapter we will consider the relationship between acidities of hydrogen halides and H—X bond energies using the Born–Haber cycle.

3–2 THE BORN–HABER CYCLE

A typical Born–Haber cycle (after Max Born and Fritz Haber) consisting of five individual steps is outlined below for the ionization of a protonic acid in aqueous solution:

(1) $HA(aq) \rightleftharpoons HA(g)$ $\Delta\tilde{G}_1^\circ$
(2) $HA(g) \rightleftharpoons H \cdot (g) + A \cdot (g)$ $\Delta\tilde{G}_2^\circ$
(3) $H \cdot (g) \rightleftharpoons H^+(g) + e^-$ $\Delta\tilde{G}_3^\circ$ or   IP
(4) $A \cdot (g) + e^- \rightleftharpoons A^-(g)$ $\Delta\tilde{G}_4^\circ$ or $-EA$
(5) $H^+(g) + A^-(g) \rightleftharpoons H^+(aq) + A^-(aq)$ $\Delta\tilde{G}_5^\circ$

Each step can be characterized by a certain standard molar free energy change, and the sum of the free energy changes for the five

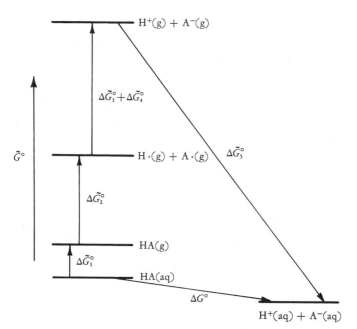

FIGURE 3–1   A Born–Haber cycle for the ionization of an acid in water. The validity of a Born–Haber cycle rests on the fact that the free energy of ionization ($\Delta\tilde{G}^\circ$) is independent of the path chosen. In the present case the path consists of vaporization of the acid from aqueous solution ($\Delta\tilde{G}_1^\circ$), symmetrical dissociation of the HA bond ($\Delta\tilde{G}_2^\circ$), ionization of H· ($\Delta\tilde{G}_3^\circ$), acquisition of an electron by A· ($\Delta\tilde{G}_4^\circ$), and solvation of the ions H^+ and A^-. Note that the latter is expected to be a large negative number. The overall free energy of ionization may turn out to be either a negative or a positive number.

steps is equal to the standard molar free energy change for the ionization of the acid in solution. This follows from the fact that G is a state function and hence is totally independent of the path that is traversed. Step (1) consists of the vaporization of the acid from solution. Step (2) is the symmetrical dissociation of the gaseous acid into its constituents, a hydrogen atom (H·) and A·, an atom or free radical. The third step represents the loss of an electron by the hydrogen atom; the free energy change for this process is referred to as an ionization potential (IP). The IP of the hydrogen atom has been measured as 13.6 eV or 313 kcal mole^{-1}; it can also be computed very accurately. Step (4) is the acquisition of an electron by A· to give an anion; the free energy change for this process is the negative of the electron affinity (EA) of A· and is usually in the range 0 to -90 kcal mole^{-1}. Unfortunately, not many electron affinities are accurately known. Finally, in order to bring the system to the desired state, we must transfer hydrogen ions and the associated anions from the vapor phase to the solution phase. The standard free energies involved in these processes are the free energies of solvation of H$^+$ and A$^-$, quantities which, unfortunately, are very difficult to extract from experimental data. As shown in Figure 3–1, however, it is expected that the solvation free energy $\Delta \tilde{G}_5°$ will have a large negative value.

3–3 EVALUATION OF THE BORN–HABER TERMS

In principle, evaluation of $\Delta \tilde{G}_1°$ is straightforward. One can establish equilibrium between the gaseous acid and the acid in dilute aqueous solution. Under these conditions we may write

$$\mu_{\text{HA(aq)}} = \mu_{\text{HA(g)}} \tag{3–1}$$

or

$$\tilde{G}°(\text{aq}) + 2.303RT \log [\text{HA}] = \tilde{G}°(\text{g}) + 2.303RT \log P_{\text{HA}} \tag{3–2}$$

Rearranging Equation (3–2) gives

$$\tilde{G}°(\text{g}) - \tilde{G}°(\text{aq}) = \Delta \tilde{G}_1° = -2.303RT \log \frac{P_{\text{HA}}}{[\text{HA}]} \tag{3–3}$$

Experimental measurement of $\Delta\tilde{G}_1{}^\circ$ then reduces essentially to determinations of the equilibrium vapor pressure and the concentration in solution. We might ask how the vapor pressure may be measured for cases where the acid is somewhat nonvolatile, that is, where P_{HA} is small. If we take the case of a carboxylic acid, there are several experimental tools which we may employ. We may prepare the acid with a radioactive ^{14}C-label, and then measure the radioactivity of the vapor phase over the solution, thus ascertaining the concentration of the acid in the vapor. Another method is to use some spectroscopic means of identification; infrared spectroscopy is extremely useful in this respect. A chemical means of determining the amount of acid vapor present is to condense a large sample of the mixture of water and acid vapor, after isolating the vapor from the system, and to titrate the acid present.

In usual practice, the Born–Haber cycle is not analyzed in terms of free energies, but rather in terms of enthalpies. To do this the methods of thermochemistry must be employed, and an illustration of this will be given in the discussion of the second step of the cycle. The use of enthalpies is convenient because for some of the steps entropies are difficult to obtain. From Equation (3–3) we can write

$$\frac{\Delta\tilde{G}_1{}^\circ}{T} = \frac{\Delta\tilde{H}_1{}^\circ}{T} - \Delta\tilde{S}_1{}^\circ = -2.303R \log \frac{P_{HA}}{[HA]} \qquad (3\text{–}4)$$

Equation (3–4) says that if we measure the temperature variation in vapor pressure of the acid over a solution of fixed concentration, and plot the logarithm of the vapor pressure against $1/T$, the slope of the line will be a linear function of the enthalpy of vaporization. The validity of this method rests on the assumption of essential invariance of $\Delta\tilde{H}_1{}^\circ$ and $\Delta\tilde{S}_1{}^\circ$ with respect to temperature. This in turn implies constancy of the heat capacities. In fact, for many substances in the temperature range of -50 to $150°C$, there is very little variation in heat capacities. Independent measurements of log P versus $1/T$ for many substances have, furthermore, given linear plots.[1]

---

[1] A good example showing this is the variation of the vapor pressure of water with temperature; see H. B. Gray and G. P. Haight, Jr., *Basic Principles of Chemistry*, p. 73, W. A. Benjamin, Inc., New York, 1967.

The second step of the Born–Haber cycle consists of the symmetrical scission of the acid to give two species, a hydrogen atom and a free radical.

$$HA(g) \rightleftharpoons H\cdot(g) + A\cdot(g) \qquad \Delta \tilde{G}_2^{\circ}$$

For this step it is also easier to measure the enthalpy rather than the free energy change. The logical way to do this might be to establish equilibrium between the three species involved, and to directly measure the equilibrium constant at some temperature. However, this is difficult to do because K for a step such as this one is likely to be extremely small. Actually, even though there are several very sensitive tools which we could use to measure the equilibrium concentration of, say, hydrogen atoms, the real reason K is not measured directly is in fact because it is difficult to bring the system to a state of equilibrium. Each of the species H· and A· has a strong tendency to undergo other reactions. For example, A· may undergo dimerization:

$$A\cdot + A\cdot \rightleftharpoons A - A$$

Thus, it is not feasible to try to use a static method of analysis for H· and A· if each of these species is doing other chemistry.

At this point the methods of thermochemistry are brought into play. To illustrate, let us suppose that HA is hydrogen chloride. The following three equilibria are relatively simple and values of the enthalpies can be obtained experimentally without too much difficulty:

(a) $2HCl(g) \rightleftharpoons H_2(g) + Cl_2(g) \qquad \Delta H_a^{\circ}$

(b) $Cl_2(g) \rightleftharpoons 2Cl\cdot(g) \qquad \Delta H_b^{\circ}$

(c) $H_2(g) \rightleftharpoons 2H\cdot(g) \qquad \Delta H_c^{\circ}$

If these three equations are added, there results

$$2HCl(g) \rightleftharpoons 2Cl\cdot(g) + 2H\cdot(g)$$

But because enthalpy is a state function, it follows that

$$\tfrac{1}{2}(\Delta H_a^{\circ} + \Delta H_b^{\circ} + \Delta H_c^{\circ}) = \Delta \tilde{H}_2^{\circ} \qquad (3\text{-}5)$$

This is the essence of Hess's law; this law merely reaffirms that the enthalpy change for a reaction is independent of the path.

Step (3) in the Born–Haber cycle is the one which is known most exactly:

$$H \cdot (g) \rightleftharpoons H^+(g) + e^- \qquad \Delta \tilde{G}_3{}^{\circ}$$

The free energy change or the enthalpy change can be accurately measured by spectroscopic means or by means of a mass spectrometer. Alternatively, we can calculate with the aid of quantum theory the ionization potential of the hydrogen atom to any desired degree of accuracy. However, reflection will reveal that this step is the one for which we will have the least use. Since the purpose of the Born–Haber data is ultimately to *compare* the strengths of acids with bond dissociation energies, it seems reasonable to expect such comparisons to be independent of the ionization of the hydrogen atom in much the same way that *relative* activity constants are independent of hydrogen ion activity.

Measurement of the enthalpy or free energy change for the fourth step of the cycle is difficult.

$$A \cdot (g) + e^- \rightleftharpoons A^-(g) \qquad \Delta \tilde{G}_4{}^{\circ}$$

In some instances dating back to as early as the 1930's, the free energy change had been obtained by measuring the equilibrium constant directly. In the case of simple halide ions the analytical tool which has been used is the high conductivity of electrons as compared to ions in the vapor phase. The more common method of obtaining $\Delta \tilde{G}_4{}^{\circ}$, however, is to measure the ultraviolet absorption spectrum of the anion. A typical spectrum will resemble a series of sharp lines followed by a continuum, as shown in Figure 3–2.

By noting the frequency at which the continuum begins, one can calculate the ionization potential for the anion. Denoting this frequency as ν_0, then the ionization potential is simply

$$IP_{A^-} = h\nu_0 \quad \text{and} \quad EA_{A\cdot} = IP_{A^-} \qquad (3\text{--}6)$$

where h is Planck's constant and has the value 6.626×10^{-27} erg sec. The ultraviolet method is not very precise, but is presently the source of most data on electron affinities.

Step (5) consists of the free energy of solvation of the individual ions, and a logical way to obtain $\Delta \tilde{G}_5{}^{\circ}$ would be to take H^+ ions in the gas phase and measure their free energy of solvation and then do

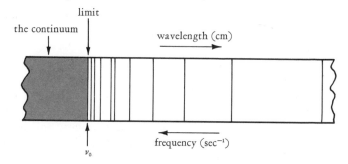

FIGURE 3-2 Diagram of an ultraviolet absorption spectrum. The scale may be calibrated in units of frequency (sec⁻¹), wavelength (cm), or wavenumber (cm⁻¹). At the point where the frequency $\nu = \nu_0$, the energy is sufficient to cause ionization of an electron.

the same for A^- ions. Here again, however, we have the familiar problem that any sort of measurement would necessarily involve measuring the free energy of solvation of at least two ions concurrently.

If we take the case of the hydrogen halides, there is the additional problem of how to obtain H^+ and X^- ions in the gas phase in order to make a measurement of solvation energy. That is, in the gas phase H^+ and X^- ions do not exist for any significant length of time. Therefore, when gaseous HCl, for example, is dissolved in water, what we are really measuring is the free energy change for the following reaction:

$$HCl(g) \rightleftharpoons H^+(aq) + Cl^-(aq)$$

It seems more reasonable that we should just be concerned with *differences* between the heats of solvation of HA and HB, since ultimately we want to compare this difference with the *difference* in acid strengths of HA and HB. If the free energy of solvation of H^+ can be assumed to be about equal in the two cases, then we will have a measure of the free energy difference of solvation between A^- and B^-.

Experimentally, the assumption mentioned above is reasonably good. It might seem possible then to obtain the free energy difference of solvation between A^- and B^- by measuring separately the heats of solution of salts, such as NaA and NaB, to form very dilute aqueous solutions, and then subtracting the two quantities. This is not desirable, however, because the reference point in this case is not the gas phase but the crystalline salts, and variations in crystal energies need not parallel variations in the energies of ions in the gas phase. Furthermore, most crystal energies are not obtained completely independently of present considerations since they are also usually arrived at by evaluating Born–Haber cycles. The crystal energy of sodium chloride, for example, would be obtained from the following set of energies:

$$
\begin{array}{ccc}
\text{NaCl(s)} \xrightarrow{\Delta H^\circ_{cryst}} & \text{Na}^+(g) + \text{Cl}^-(g) & \\
\Big\downarrow -\Delta H_f^\circ \quad \Big\uparrow \text{IP} & & \Big\uparrow -\text{EA} \\
\text{Na(s)} \xrightarrow{\Delta H^\circ_{subl}} \text{Na·(g)} & & \\
+\tfrac{1}{2}\text{Cl}_2(g) \xrightarrow{\;\tfrac{1}{2}\text{DE}\;} & \text{Cl·(g)} &
\end{array}
$$

$$\Delta H^\circ_{cryst} = -\Delta H_f^\circ(\text{NaCl}) + \Delta H^\circ_{subl} + \tfrac{1}{2}\text{DE} + \text{IP} - \text{EA}$$

where

ΔH°_{subl} is the heat of sublimation of Na(s),
DE is the symmetrical dissociation energy of $\text{Cl}_2(g)$,
IP is the ionization potential of Na·(g),
EA is the electron affinity of Cl·(g),
ΔH°_{cryst} is the crystalline lattice enthalpy of NaCl(s).

In practice what is usually done then is to measure the heats of solution of the hydrogen halides, and by arbitrarily setting the free energy of solvation of H^+ at zero, one can obtain values for each of the halide ions. The additional assumption is made, when doing this, that there is no molecular HX present in solution which would also be solvated. One way of seeing whether the contribution due to H^+ does in fact drop out is to measure the heat of mixing of dilute aqueous NaA and NaB solutions. The fact that there is experimentally no significant heat of mixing means that the solvation of A^- takes place essentially independent of the solvation of B^-, that is, that there are no important interactions between the ions.

TABLE 3-1
Born-Haber Data for the Hydrohalic Acids[a]

	HF	HCl	HBr	HI
$\Delta \tilde{H}_1°$, kcal mole^{-1}	12	4	5	6
$\Delta \tilde{H}_2°$, kcal mole^{-1}	135	103	88	71
$\Delta \tilde{H}_3°$, kcal mole^{-1}	313	313	313	313
$\Delta \tilde{H}_4°$, kcal mole^{-1}	−80	−83	−77	−70
$\Delta \tilde{H}_5°$, kcal mole^{-1}	−382	−349	−341	−330
$T \Delta \tilde{S}°_{1-4}$, kcal mole^{-1}	14	12	13	13
$T \Delta \tilde{S}°_5$, kcal mole^{-1}	−20	−16	−15	−14
$\Delta \tilde{G}°$, kcal mole^{-1}	4	−8	−10	−9
pK (calc)	3	−6	−7	−7

[a] Data taken from H. B. Gray and G. P. Haight, Jr., *Basic Principles of Chemistry*, pp. 238, 393, W. A. Benjamin, Inc., New York, 1967.

Returning again to the hydrogen halides, the above table lists enthalpy differences for various steps of the Born–Haber cycle.

A cursory inspection of Table 3-1 reveals that the numbers for the second step of the Born–Haber cycle, which is the dissociation of the hydrogen halides, follow a monotonic trend and that hydrogen fluoride, the only weak acid of the lot, possesses an exceptionally strong bond. However, it is obvious that the bond energies alone do not serve as a simple source of predictions of acidities. Note, for example, that there is a large drop in bond energy between HBr and HI which is not reflected in any large change in acidity. The next point to note is the fact that the large numbers in Table 3-1, the bond dissociation energy plus the ionization potential, and the electron affinity plus the heat of solution of the ions, almost cancel each other. Consequently, all the small numbers exert important influences on the comparison that we set out to make. We can say that the influence of the very strong H—F bond on the relative acidity of HF is almost matched by the very large, negative free energy of solution of fluoride ions, but that this matching allows the full influence of the high heat of vaporization of hydrogen fluoride from water solution to be effective in stabilizing the neutral HF molecules in water. Another way of saying the same thing is to point out that the very high negative enthalpy of solution of fluoride ions is partially compensated for by a relatively large negative enthalpy of solution of hydrogen fluoride molecules.

Our presentation may seem confusing and frustrating. This is true if one takes the point of view that we want to "understand" acidity constants by breaking the ionization process into steps. This approach implies that for some reason the steps in the Born–Haber cycle are more "fundamental" than the acidity constants. In fact, in this sense all the data are entirely equivalent; of course, some numbers are known more accurately than others. If all the other factors canceled exactly, we would expect that there would be a simple proportionality between bond dissociation energies in HA molecules and the ionization constants, a comparison that was chosen arbitrarily in setting up the problem. The final result, after examination of the best data that we have, is the conclusion that comparison of bond dissociation energies and acidity constants, where both are known, probably provides a reasonable way to *determine* less accessible quantities, such as the electron affinities of atoms.

At this point we should make a confession. The acidity constants for HCl, HBr, and HI cannot be measured directly in water solution. The extent of ionization in each case is so large that no significant measure of the concentrations of the neutral molecules in dilute water solutions can be obtained. Ionization of the hydrogen halides in other solvents, such as ethyl alcohol or acetic acid, has been studied and HCl, HBr, and HI appear to have nearly equal acidities, and to be much more extensively dissociated than HF. In fact, the acidities of the three heavier hydrogen halides in water can only be obtained by estimates based upon extrapolation from other solvents or on some analysis such as the Born–Haber cycle. The values that we have listed (p. 26) are numbers we have obtained from an analysis presented in the next chapter.

We have gone through an exercise for pedagogical reasons. It might have made more sense to discuss ionization constants for a series of weak acids for which pK values are well known. Unfortunately, there are so few data available for electron affinities of anions that we would still have been unable to close the cycles satisfactorily. In the next chapter we will develop an energy cycle that will bypass electron affinities and anion solvation free energies and will allow us to estimate aqueous-solution pK values for HCl, HBr, and HI with reasonable accuracy.

EXERCISES

1. The following problem shows how one might experimentally determine the $\Delta \tilde{G}_1°$ discussed in the text.

(a) For a very dilute solution of an acid HA, show that its concentration in moles per liter may be approximated by

$$[HA] = \frac{N_{HA} \, \rho}{MW_{HA}}$$

where N_{HA} is the mole fraction of acid, ρ is the density of the solvent in grams per liter, and MW_{HA} is the molecular weight of the acid.

(b) Recall also for very dilute solutions that the vapor pressure of a volatile solute over the solution is directly proportional to the mole fraction of the solute (Henry's Law). Using the results of part (a), show that for a dilute aqueous solution of an acid HA at 25°C

$$\Delta \tilde{G}_1° = 40.8 - 13.6 \log (k \cdot MW_{HA}) \text{ kcal mole}^{-1}$$

where k is the Henry's law constant.

2. In the energy cycle depicted for sodium chloride on p. 25, $\Delta H°_{cryst}$ is the lattice enthalpy of the crystal. Such enthalpies of crystal formation from gaseous ions are difficult to measure directly, but are nearly equal to $\Delta E°_{cryst}$, which can be calculated reasonably well using an electrostatic treatment. If we suppose that the potential energy (PE) of a pair of ions with opposite unit charges (such as K^+ and F^-) is given by an expression

$$PE = -\frac{e^2}{r} + \frac{B}{r^n}$$

where e is the charge of the electron, B is a constant, and r is the separation between the ions, show that a stable configuration of these two ions occurs at an energy PE_{min} when $r = R$ and

$$PE_{min} = \frac{e^2}{R}\left(1 - \frac{1}{n}\right)$$

3. The factor by which we should multiply the potential energy of a single ion pair in order to obtain the lattice energy is $N \times A$ where N is

Avogadro's number and A is a constant, dependent only upon the crystal geometry, called the *Madelung constant.* For the cubic NaCl-type lattice this constant has the value 1.748. Using the results of Problem 2 with $n = 9$, plus the fact that the equilibrium lithium-fluorine distance in LiF (cubic) is 2.009, estimate the lattice energy of this alkali halide and compare with the experimental data given in Problem 4.

4. The following data are enthalpies of formation of the alkali metal fluoride and iodides in kilocalories per mole:

	Li	Na	K	Rb	Cs
Fluoride	145.7	136.3	134.5	131.8	130.3
Iodide	64.8	68.8	78.3	79	83.9

Cesium iodide is thus the most stable iodide, while cesium fluoride is the least stable fluoride.

(a) Why should you expect that in the case of the iodides the heats of sublimation of the metals and the ionization potentials of the metallic atoms rather than the lattice energies should make the major contributions in the Born–Haber scheme, while in the case of the fluorides probably the reverse is true?

(b) The following lattice energies (in kilocalories per mole, for the fluorides are the experimental results from a Born–Haber analysis:

LiF	NaF	KF	RbF	CsF
242.8	216.6	191.8	184.6	176.0

Plot these against the enthalpy information given above to see how good the correlation actually is.

5. What experimental data would you need in order to estimate the proton affinity of gaseous water molecules?

$$H_2O(g) + H^+(g) \rightleftharpoons H_3O^+(g)$$

6. Consider the ionization of a simple acid such as HCl in the gas phase and in aqueous solution.

$$HCl(g) \rightleftharpoons H^+(g) + Cl^-(g)$$
$$HCl(aq) \rightleftharpoons H^+(aq) + Cl^-(aq)$$

The first process has a *positive* standard entropy change (about 23 eu) whereas the second has a *negative* standard entropy change (about −13 eu). See if you can think of a reason for this sign reversal.

IV

Energetics of Acid Ionization in a Cycle Including Electroreduction Potentials

4-1 INTRODUCTION

In the last chapter we analyzed the relationship between ionization constants of acids, HA, and the dissociation energies of H—A bonds. Although the crudity of some of the data and important variations in quantities such as solvation energies and electron affinities complicate the correlation, there is an obvious relationship between the great strength of the H—F bond and the fact that hydrogen fluoride is a much weaker acid than the other hydrogen halides. There should be many other series of reactions of halogen-containing compounds that can be related to both bond energies and acidities.

A major uncertainty in the Born–Haber cycle is the energetics of solution of the ions, which can be avoided by choice of some other reaction carried out in water solution to compare with acid ionization. We will now examine such a reaction.

Consider the ionization of two acids in aqueous solution.

$$HA(aq) \rightleftharpoons H^+(aq) + A^-(aq)$$
$$HB(aq) \rightleftharpoons H^+(aq) + B^-(aq)$$

[31]

Each of these processes may be partitioned into the following three steps:

Acid HA $\quad$ $\begin{array}{ll} \text{HA(aq)} \rightarrow \text{H·(aq)} + \text{A·(aq)} & \Delta \tilde{G_1}°(\text{A}) \\ \text{H·(aq)} \rightarrow \text{H}^+(\text{aq}) + e^- & \Delta \tilde{G_2}° \\ \text{A·(aq)} + e^- \rightarrow \text{A}^-(\text{aq}) & \Delta \tilde{G_3}°(\text{A}) \end{array}$

Acid HB $\quad$ $\begin{array}{ll} \text{HB(aq)} \rightarrow \text{H·(aq)} + \text{B·(aq)} & \Delta \tilde{G_1}°(\text{B}) \\ \text{H·(aq)} \rightarrow \text{H}^+(\text{aq}) + e^- & \Delta \tilde{G_2}° \\ \text{B·(aq)} + e^- \rightarrow \text{B}^-(\text{aq}) & \Delta \tilde{G_3}°(\text{B}) \end{array}$

Therefore, it follows that $\Delta \tilde{G}°$ for the proton-transfer reaction

$$\text{HB(aq)} + \text{A}^-(\text{aq}) \rightleftharpoons \text{HA(aq)} + \text{B}^-(\text{aq})$$

can be written as

$$\Delta \tilde{G}° = \Delta \tilde{G_1}°(\text{B}) + \Delta \tilde{G_3}°(\text{B}) - \Delta \tilde{G_1}°(\text{A}) - \Delta \tilde{G_3}°(\text{A}) \quad (4\text{-}1)$$

The term $\Delta \tilde{G_2}°$ does not appear in this expression since this step is common to both acids.

Let us now examine what might appear to be an entirely unrelated reaction, the electrochemical reduction of the diatomic molecules A_2 and B_2 in solution.

$$\begin{array}{ll} A_2(\text{aq}) + 2e^- \rightleftharpoons 2\text{A}^-(\text{aq}) & \mathcal{E}_\text{A} \\ B_2(\text{aq}) + 2e^- \rightleftharpoons 2\text{B}^-(\text{aq}) & \mathcal{E}_\text{B} \end{array}$$

Each of these processes may be dissected into two simpler steps:

$$\begin{array}{ll} A_2(\text{aq}) \rightleftharpoons 2\text{A·(aq)} & \Delta \tilde{G_4}°(\text{A}) \\ 2\text{A·(aq)} + 2e^- \rightleftharpoons 2\text{A}^-(\text{aq}) & 2\,\Delta \tilde{G_3}°(\text{A}) \\ B_2(\text{aq}) \rightleftharpoons 2\text{B·(aq)} & \Delta \tilde{G_4}°(\text{B}) \\ 2\text{B·(aq)} + 2e^- \rightleftharpoons 2\text{B}^-(\text{aq}) & 2\,\Delta \tilde{G_3}°(\text{B}) \end{array}$$

Thus, Equation (4-1) may be rewritten as follows:

$$\Delta \tilde{G}° = [\Delta \tilde{G_1}°(\text{B}) - \Delta \tilde{G_1}°(\text{A})] + \tfrac{1}{2}(\mathcal{E}_\text{B} - \mathcal{E}_\text{A}) \\ - \tfrac{1}{2}[\Delta \tilde{G_4}°(\text{B}) - \Delta \tilde{G_4}°(\text{A})] \quad (4\text{-}2)$$

This equation is seen to consist of "bond energy" terms and electroreduction potentials. It is important to note that there are no electron affinity and solvation energy terms; this is advantageous since these data are difficult to obtain and are usually somewhat imprecise anyway. Another point to be made is that we do not have available directly the free energies of dissociation of A_2 and B_2 in the solution phase. We may assume for the present, however, that the entropies of dissociation in solution will be similar for the series of halogen molecules; therefore, we may expect the enthalpies of dissociation in the gas phase to parallel the free energies of dissociation in the solution phase. We will, furthermore, use the same sort of reasoning for the dissociation of HA molecules. If such entropies are required for more elaborate work, they may be measured experimentally or estimated using the methods of statistical mechanics. The overall procedure for estimation of $\Delta \tilde{G}^{\circ}$ is shown schematically in Figure 4–1.

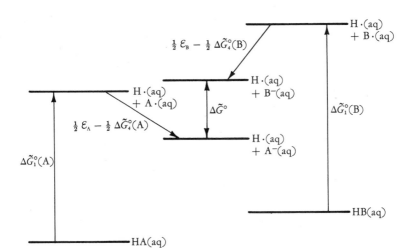

FIGURE 4–1   Pair of Born–Haber cycles for the proton-exchange reaction $HB(aq) + A^-(aq) \rightleftharpoons HA(aq) + B^-(aq)$.   The problem of obtaining reliable values of solvation energies and of electron affinities is circumvented by (a) using gas phase values for the symmetrical dissociation of the acids in solution, and (b) obtaining the electron affinity data indirectly from electroreduction potentials.

4-2   MEASUREMENT OF REDUCTION
POTENTIALS

Before examining the available data, it might be worthwhile to digress and consider how the electroreduction potentials $\mathcal{E}_A$ and $\mathcal{E}_B$ are experimentally determined.   If a zinc rod is inserted into a solution of some zinc salt and a copper rod inserted into a solution of some copper salt and the two solutions connected by means of an outer circuit and also by means of a potassium chloride salt bridge (see Figure 4–2), then in this *electrochemical cell* there will be a flow of current in the outer circuit.   The direction of current flow is dependent upon the concentration of solutions and also upon their temperature.   If an applied external voltage is inserted into the circuit and is adjusted so as to prevent any current from flowing in either direction, then the system is clearly at equilibrium and a

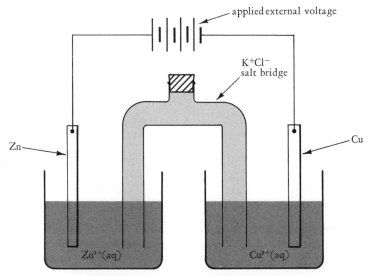

FIGURE 4-2   An electrochemical cell.

balance has been established between the electrical and chemical potentials. At equilibrium we have

$$Zn(s) + Cu^{2+}(aq) \rightleftharpoons Zn^{2+}(aq) + Cu(s)$$

so that this balance of potentials can be expressed as

$$\mu_{Zn(s)} + \mu_{Cu^{2+}(aq)} = \mu_{Zn^{2+}(aq)} + \mu_{Cu(s)} + \phi \qquad (4\text{-}3)$$

where ϕ is the applied potential and must have units of energy per mole of reaction. This is just the net work involved in passing current to accomplish the conversion of 1 g-atom of zinc and 1 mole of copper (II) ions to 1 mole of zinc (II) ions and 1 g-atom of copper. In other words, ϕ is really the chemical potential of electrons, which may be related to the free energy change of the reaction as follows:

$$\Delta G = \phi \Delta n_e \qquad (4\text{-}4)$$

where Δn_e is the change in the number of moles of electrons.

When the ions are at unit activities and the electrodes are pure metals, Equation (4-4) can be rewritten equivalently as

$$\Delta G^\circ = -n\mathcal{E}^\circ \mathcal{F} \qquad (4\text{-}5)$$

where

n is the electron change per molecule of reaction,

$\mathcal{E}^\circ$ is the potential of the cathode minus the potential of the anode, by convention,

$\mathcal{F}$ is the faraday; the amount of electricity required for 1 mole of reaction where n is unity. It has the approximate value of 96,500 coulombs. Since 1 volt-coulomb equals 1 joule, and 4.184 joules equals 1 calorie, it follows that 1 volt-coulomb is approximately equal to 0.24 calorie.

As written, $\mathcal{E}^\circ$ is a difference in electrode potentials. It is possible, however, to tabulate a series of single electrode potentials by arbitrarily assigning the potential of the hydrogen electrode to be zero.

$$2H^+(aq; 1 \text{ molar}) + 2e^- \rightleftharpoons H_2(s; 1 \text{ atm})$$
$$\mathcal{E}_{H^+/H_2} = 0 \text{ V}$$

By measuring the potentials of other half-reactions and expressing them relative to the hydrogen electrode, it is possible to construct

TABLE 4-1

Data for the Estimation of Ionization Energetics for the Hydrohalic Acids[a]

Halogen	Bond dissociation energy, H—A (kcal mole⁻¹)	Bond dissociation energy, A—A (kcal mole⁻¹)	Reduction potential		Calculated $\Delta \tilde{G}°$ (kcal mole⁻¹)	Calculated[b] pK
			$\mathcal{E}°$ ($V_{A_2/2A}-$)	$-n\mathfrak{F}\mathcal{E}°$ (kcal)		
F	135	37	+2.87	−132	(0)	(3)
Cl	103	58	+1.36	− 62	− 8	− 9
Br	88	46	+1.07	− 50	−11	−11
I	71	36	+0.53	− 24	− 9	−10

[a] Conductivity measurements in glacial acetic acid by Kolthoff and Willman (1934) revealed the acidity trend $HClO_4 > HBr > H_2SO_4 > HCl > HNO_2$. More recent measurements in this solvent by Schwarzenbach (1959) showed that HBr and HCl have pw values (pw is a quantity similar, but not identical, to pK) of −6.8 and −5.6, respectively. A value for HI could not be obtained due to the fact that it is unstable in acetic acid at concentrations greater than 90%. Hydrofluoric acid was not investigated in this solvent.

[b] A constant of 4 kcal mole⁻¹ was added to each of the $\Delta \tilde{G}°$ values in order that the calculated pK for HF would coincide with the experimentally known value.

a useful table of reduction potentials. The reduction potentials for the halogens are given in Table 4-1.

4-3 ANALYSIS OF DATA

Let us now return and look once again at Equation (4-2). The term $[\Delta \tilde{G}_1°(B) - \Delta \tilde{G}_1°(A)]$ is a measure of the difference in strengths of the two H—A bonds. The values of $\Delta \tilde{G}_1°$ pertain to dissociations carried out in solution, and while these data might not be identical to those obtained for gas phase scissions, we might expect the trends to remain the same.

The second term in parentheses represents the difference in electrochemical reduction potentials for A_2 and B_2. This difference, as explained in the previous section, is a quantity which can be obtained experimentally rather easily.

The last term also represents a bond energy difference; it is a measure of the difference in the energies for the A—A and B—B bonds. The cleavage is to be carried out in solution, but we would nevertheless expect again that trends will remain invariant upon going to the gas phase where data are much more easily obtainable.

Data presented in Table 4–1 have been taken from the literature using the assumptions just discussed. In spite of the several assumptions which have been made, the calculated trend of acidities satisfactorily reproduces that known from experimental measurements in nonaqueous solvents. We may conclude, therefore, that reasonable estimates may be made of the strengths of the hydrohalic acids using as the key term in the energy cycle the electroreduction potentials for the corresponding halogens.

The electroreduction potentials decrease regularly as we pass from fluorine to iodine; this would probably be expected intuitively because the lighter halogens have the greater affinities for electrons. However, it is also interesting to note that the halogen bond energies are fairly close together and do not fit a regular pattern. Part of the reason for the very great oxidizing power of fluorine derives from the fact that the F—F bond is very weak. This stands in striking contrast to the influence of the H—A bond energies on the acid ionization constants, where a major factor in making hydrogen fluoride a weak acid is the great strength of the H—F bond. Table 4–1 also summarizes the bond energy relationships in the halogens and hydrogen halides. Correlation of these simple dissociation reactions with each other highlights the irregularities noted. A major challenge is posed for theoretical structural chemists by the anomalous strength of the H—F bond and weakness of the F—F bond. Reasonably satisfactory rationalizations of the remarkable effects have been supplied, but require rather sophisticated analyses of the details of electronic interactions in the molecules.

EXERCISES

1. Using appropriate gas phase data determine whether bromine or chlorine should be the stronger oxidant. Does this same order prevail in aqueous solution?

2. Using relationships you learned earlier during the study of the decomposition of phosphorus pentachloride, derive the Nernst equation:

$$\varepsilon = \varepsilon^\circ - \frac{2.303RT}{n\mathfrak{F}} \log K_{eq}$$

3. If 15 amperes of current are passed for 0.796 hours through an electrolysis cell containing a $ZnSO_4$ solution, how many grams of metallic zinc will be deposited at the cathode?

4. Tabulated reduction half-cell potentials for the Cu^{2+}/Cu couple and the Zn^{2+}/Zn couple are $+0.332$ V and -0.763 V, respectively. Calculate the equilibrium constant for the reaction

$$Cu^{2+}(aq) + Zn(s) \rightleftharpoons Cu(s) + Zn^{2+}(aq)$$

at 25°C, and convince yourself of one very useful application of electrochemistry.

5. An electrochemical cell which transforms the chemical energy of a fuel directly into electrical energy is called a *fuel cell*. Suppose we decide to design a fuel cell using hydrogen gas as the fuel and oxygen gas as the oxidant. By reference to tables of reduction potentials, estimate the potential of this cell if it is to operate at 25°C and 1 atm.

6. A plot of potential versus pH is a useful graphic device for depicting the oxidation-reduction and acid-base behavior of an element in a concise manner. Consider the following general equation

$$ox + ne^- + mH^+ \rightleftharpoons red$$

where ox and red refer to the oxidized and reduced forms of some metal. Derive a relationship between the cell potential and the pH of the solution.

7. For a simple reduction

$$ox_1 + red_2 \rightleftharpoons red_1 + ox_2$$

involving transfer of one electron, what must be the ε° if the reaction is to be complete to the extent that

$$\frac{[red_1]}{[ox_1]} = \frac{[ox_2]}{[red_2]} = 1000$$

when equilibrium is reached?

8. The half-cell potential for the half-reaction

$$Ag^+(aq) + e^- \rightleftharpoons Ag(s)$$

is $+0.799$ V, and the solubility product for silver iodide is 1.5×10^{-16}. Calculate the half-cell potential for the reaction

$$AgI(s) + e^- \rightleftharpoons Ag(s) + I^-(aq)$$

9. What sort of experimental data would be needed if we wanted to analyze energetics in a Born–Haber scheme for several M^{2+}/M° couples?

V

Rate Phenomena in Chemical
Reactivity

5-1 INTRODUCTION

In the previous four chapters we have discussed chemical energetics as a measure of reactivity. Boundary conditions on reactions are supplied by thermodynamics. A reaction can only proceed until equilibrium is established. If the molar heat of the reaction is positive, the reaction may be pushed farther by raising the temperature and establishing a new equilibrium relationship more favorable to reaction products.[1]

However, we are all thoroughly familiar with the fact that reactions are often so slow that for all practical purposes they do not occur. In others the approach of a system to chemical equilibrium occurs at a rate that is easily observed, and in still other cases equilibrium is established so rapidly that the rate cannot be observed using ordinary techniques. The following are randomly chosen examples:

---

[1] Specification of forward and reverse reactions is of course arbitrary, since any reaction can be turned around so the meaning of products and reactants is reversed. We use the usual convention in which the materials appearing on the right-hand side of the equation are called products.

Too slow to observe under any known conditions:

$$2H_2CO \rightleftharpoons CH_4 + CO_2$$
Formaldehyde   Methane   Carbon Dioxide

Reaction slow but readily observable:

Moisture
$$4Fe + 3O_2 \rightarrow 2Fe_2O_3$$
(Rusting of Iron)

Equilibrium established very rapidly:

$$H_2O + H_2SO_4 \rightleftharpoons H_3O^+ + HSO_4^-$$
$$H_2O + HSO_4^- \rightleftharpoons H_3O^+ + SO_4^{2-}$$

There are also many examples of reactions having rates that are very sensitive to the reaction conditions. For example, a mixture of methane and oxygen does not react at an observable rate, but if the gaseous mixture is passed over a gauze made of fine platinum wire, reaction to produce carbon dioxide and water occurs very rapidly. Furthermore, it is fairly obvious that the reaction occurs on the surface of the platinum, because the heat of the reaction is sufficient to raise the temperature of the gauze to white heat. This principle is used in Coleman lamps, which are commonly used by campers.

Control of the rates of chemical reactions is one of the most important tools that man has in his struggle to control his environment; and the kinetic aspects of thermodynamics provide such controls. The free energies of reactions, on the other hand, are immutable natural constants, which must be understood in order to understand our limitations. We can never find catalysts that will allow us to "run a reaction uphill." In fact, a catalyst can never influence the position of equilibrium in a system, only the rate of establishment of equilibrium. This observation is a matter of experience and is also a corollary of the *principle of microscopic reversibility*, which states that in a system at equilibrium, reaction along any path must proceed at the same rate in both directions. Consequently, we realize that catalysts must affect both forward and reverse reaction rates in the same way.

Study of reaction rates poses deep and fascinating questions. What happens when two stable molecules approach each other and undergo reaction? How are the bonds broken and formed as the old molecules are destroyed and the new products formed? Why does a small change in reaction conditions, such as irradiation with a weak light source or changing the pH of a solution, sometimes change the rate of a reaction by so much as a million-fold? Answers to these fundamental questions involve two distinctly different kinds of analysis of reactions. The two fields are: (1) study of reaction mechanisms; and (2) analysis of the molecular events that occur during elementary reactions.

5–2   REACTION MECHANISMS

Many reactions occur by complex pathways, in which a series of discrete chemical changes occur in sequence. Intermediates may be formed and destroyed without ever being accumulated. Understanding of factors that control the rate of the overall process requires detailed dissection of the mechanics. Often a single step out of several can be pinpointed as the *rate-controlling step*, a reaction that is the slowest step in the entire process. Unraveling of the mechanism of a reaction is a fascinating game which can require all the experimental and intellectual ingenuity of shrewd physical scientists.

5–3   ELEMENTARY REACTIONS

An elementary reaction is a chemical change which cannot be further broken down into discrete chemical steps. Actually, the number of elementary steps in a reaction mechanism may "increase" as experimental methods are developed to subject the system to increasingly penetrating study.

Theories of reaction rates are usually formulated to describe the intimate details of elementary reactions, in the course of actual happening. This requires extension of theories of structural chemistry to situations in which molecular structures are warped so as to form distorted forms that can never be isolated for direct study. In short, the only way to study the transitional molecular species formed during an elementary reaction step is by studying rates of reactions and interpreting the results in a self-consistent manner. In very recent years remarkable strides have been taken in direct observation of the fundamental acts in elementary reactions. The method of molecular beams allows direct observations of the results of single collisions between pairs of reactive molecules.

Since the concepts involved in direct study of elementary reactions are easily visualized, and provide ideas basic to all modern rate theory, such work will be discussed briefly in the next chapter. In the following chapters we will consider studies of reaction mechanisms and the systematic variation of kinetic reactivity on molecular structure.

EXERCISES

1. List a dozen slow reactions that you know occur in nature.

2. It has been said that chemical dynamic time scales differentiate between biological and geological systems. Explain.

3. Raising the temperature of a reaction mixture usually makes reactions proceed more rapidly. List all the reasons that you can think of to account for this phenomenon. (This subject will be discussed in a later chapter.)

4. The decomposition of nitramide in water solution takes the following course:

$$H_2NNO_2 \rightarrow H_2O + N_2O$$

A very short-lived intermediate in the reaction is believed to be

Can you formulate a mechanism involving only proton transfers to generate the intermediate from nitramide? The reaction is strongly catalyzed by addition of bases. How do you imagine that bases might speed up the overall process of production of N_2O? Although we have not yet presented examples of reaction mechanistic analysis, the student should try his hand at this point. After studying the next few chapters, return to this problem and analyze it once again.

VI

Elementary Reaction Processes in Gaseous and Liquid Systems

S tructural chemistry and chemical dynamics are the two great
fields of chemistry. The phenomenal progress in structural
chemistry of recent years has not been matched by chemical dynamics; for example, we have only a primitive understanding of the
forces which act during a chemical reaction, and our knowledge of
the rates of most reactions remains largely empirical. We have
tables of rate constants but a lack of good models for what happens
on an atomic scale when such reactions occur.

6–1 RECENT EXPERIMENTAL AND THEORETICAL ADVANCES

Before 1950, research in theoretical chemical kinetics was concerned mainly with rate constants, together with their dependence
on temperature, pressure, molecular structure, and so on. With the
advent of high-speed computers the emphasis in theoretical chemical
kinetics has gradually shifted from a study of the macroscopic
aspects of a reaction to a detailed examination of the processes

actually taking place at the molecular or microscopic level. Several new and elegant types of experiments have been devised with this view in mind. These include study of gas phase reactions of small molecules, under closely controlled conditions, measurement of the rates of fast reactions in solution and at electrodes, and some interesting studies that are half-experiment and half-theory, namely, electronic computer calculations of classical mechanical collision trajectories.

The first group includes studies in shock tubes, in flash photolyses, in gaseous flow systems, and studies of crossed-molecular beams. In the crossed beam experiment (Figure 6–1), two beams of different materials are directed toward each other. In practice, one may use molecular beams having a distribution of velocities, or alternatively, one may prepare beams in which all the particles have essentially the same velocity. The scattered beam contains reaction products as well as some particles from the incident beams. By looking at

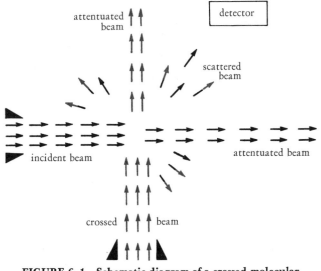

FIGURE 6–1   Schematic diagram of a crossed-molecular beam experiment.

the angular distribution and kinetic energy distribution of the products as a function of initial velocity of the reactants, powerful deductions concerning the nature of the collisional process can be made. Reactions between alkali metals and alkyl halides have been extensively studied by D. R. Herschbach and other workers using this method.

$$K \cdot + RBr \rightarrow KBr + R \cdot$$

The study of exceedingly fast reactions in solution has become an active field of research in the last decade. Indeed, it was for their pioneering efforts in this field that Manfred Eigen, George Porter, and Ronald G. W. Norrish won the 1967 Nobel prize in chemistry. Aided by increased familiarity with electronic instrumentation, chemists are able to study reactions, for example, involving only the transfer of an electron in reactions between gaseous ions and molecules. Results obtained from these studies have immediate implications in the field of electrochemical rate processes.

The presence of high-speed computers has opened up tremendous possibilities for the study of chemical dynamics. Thus, it is now possible to investigate the analytical mechanics of reactions by taking the classical mechanical equations of motion and solving them numerically to obtain descriptions of the flights of atoms and molecules undergoing chemically reactive collisions. Two uncertainties in this approximate treatment are the form of the function used to describe the potential energy of interaction as molecules approach each other, and key assumptions concerning the dynamics of change in the bonded structures of molecules. The theory is not really self-sustaining, but must be continuously related to results of experiments with colliding particles.

6-2 REACTIONS IN THE GASEOUS PHASE

It has become increasingly clear that the formation of products from reactants almost always takes place by a number of relatively simple steps in which the amount of atomic rearrangement in each step is at a minimum. These one-stage steps are called *elementary* processes, and a large part of chemical dynamics consists in the elucidation of their nature and relative importance in any given chemical reaction. All elementary reaction steps are of two kinds: *collision*, as exemplified by the reaction H + H—Br → H$_2$ + Br, and *decay*, as exemplified by the isomerization of cyclopropane to propene or the α-decay of uranium-238 nuclei. Collision, which is bimolecular (that is, two species are involved), usually precedes any decay (which is unimolecular) because it is necessary to form or activate the decaying species.

Collision and decay become easiest to discuss for the gas phase where molecules are far apart on the average and complications from interaction with a solvent are avoided. Thus, the crossed-molecular beam experiment becomes ideal for studying collisional processes in gas phase reactions. Consider the general bimolecular reaction

$$A + B \rightarrow C + D$$

A quantity of fundamental importance which we hope to get from a molecular beam experiment is the reaction cross section, $\sigma_{AB}(v)$, because it can be related in a simple way to the speed with which the reaction occurs. Mathematically, the reaction cross section is a proportionality factor which measures the likelihood of reaction when A approaches B with a relative velocity of v. If we are using beams which do not contain molecules at a nearly uniform velocity, it becomes necessary to know something about the distribution of velocities in the beam. The reaction cross section has units of an area per molecule; hence, it is convenient intuitively to regard this quantity as the "target" area of a B molecule which is presented to an approaching A molecule.

As mentioned earlier, the experimental data which one obtains directly from the beam experiment are the angular distributions of products and the attenuations of the incident beams. In this respect, the experiment resembles photometry (measurement of light absorption) in which we seek to describe the attenuation of a beam of photons passing through an absorbing medium. The rate with which reaction occurs becomes simply

$$\text{Rate} = v\sigma_{AB}(v)n_A n_B$$

where n_A is the number of A molecules per unit volume. All the information about the speed of the reaction is therefore contained in the product of the cross section times the relative velocity of A and B particles. Because the reaction cross section depends on the forces which are involved during a chemical reaction, it becomes necessary when transforming the molecular beam data into a single number, the cross section, to decide whether the dynamics involved must be treated using quantum mechanics, or whether classical mechanics (that is, Newton's laws of motion) can provide an adequate, approximate description. In the latter case we usually consider both partners in the reaction as hard spheres which undergo collisions, with reaction occurring for relative energies above a threshold E_0. This concept assumes that if two molecules are charging at each other with high enough velocities so that on "impact" the total collision energy is greater than E_0, reaction will occur. This procedure has a mathematical convenience but an aesthetic unpleasantness attached to it.

Calculations carried out by Karplus, Porter, and Sharma on the reaction

$$T + H_2 \rightarrow TH + H$$

indicate (1) the existence of a threshold energy $E_0 = 5.8$ kcal mole^{-1} such that $\sigma_{AB}(v)$ is zero for E less than E_0, (2) a rise of $\sigma_{AB}(v)$ with increasing E above the threshold to a maximum value of $\sigma_{AB}(v) = 2.4$ Å^2, and (3) a fall in $\sigma_{AB}(v)$ at still higher E. Typically, chemical reaction cross sections lie in the range 10^{-1} Å$^2 < \sigma_{AB(max)}(v) < 10^2$ Å^2 when the energy is in the range near which the cross section is a maximum. In Figure 6–2 is shown a plot of the calculated results.

To discuss decay processes adequately, it is necessary to realize that a molecule contains energy in various forms (see Figure 6–3). Some of it is in the form of translational kinetic energy. In addition, there is vibrational energy associated with the stretching and bending of bonds, rotational energy associated with rotation of the molecule as a whole and of parts of the molecule about bond axes, and electronic energy associated with the electronic configuration of the molecule. Quantum mechanics tells us that it is convenient to discuss the latter three kinds of energy in terms of discrete, quantized energy levels.

The process of decay may then be viewed simply as conversion of energy from one form to another coupled with transfer of energy

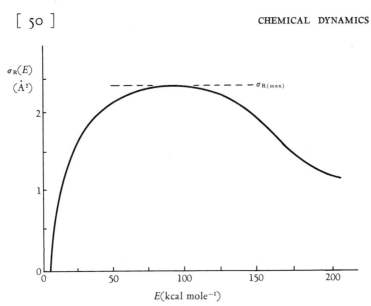

FIGURE 6-2 Theoretical calculation of the variation of the reaction cross section with relative initial kinetic energy E for the reaction T + H₂ → TH + H.

between parts of the system. The transfer may be either *intramolecular*, *intermolecular*, or involve some combination of both.

The decay of radioisotopes is a good example of such a process but is not of much interest to the chemist since it involves a nuclear change. A very common decay process is that known as *phosphorescence*, such as is observed of certain substances called phosphors. This process is deactivation of an electronically excited molecule to its ground state with a concomitant conversion of electronic energy to light energy, which is transferred to the environment in the form of emitted light.

Rates of decay follow an experimental rate law of the form:

$$\text{Rate of decay} = k[A]$$

where k is the rate constant, usually given in $\sec^{-1}$, and $[A]$ is the concentration of the decaying species.

The rate constant for phosphorescence in most organic molecules

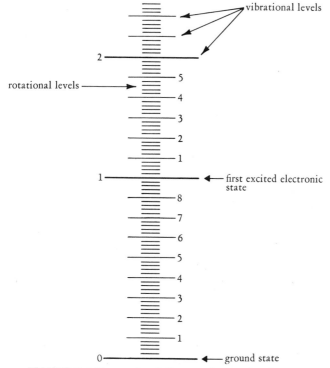

FIGURE 6-3 Energy level diagram for a molecule.

usually lies in the range of 0.1 to 1000 sec^{-1}. *Fluorescence* is decay from another kind of electronically excited state to the ground state. It occurs much faster than phosphorescence, and rate constants usually lie in the range 10^5 to 10^8 sec^{-1}. In the table below are some values for rate constants of phosphorescence (k_p) and for rate constants of fluorescence (k_f).

Consider the case of an unstable entity formed by chemical reaction

$$H\cdot + CH_3CH{=}CH_2 \rightarrow [CH_3CH_2CH_2\cdot] \rightarrow CH_3\cdot + CH_2{=}CH_2$$

| Hydrogen atom | Propylene | *n*-propyl radical | Methyl radical | Ethylene |

TABLE 6-1

Rate Constants for Phosphorescence and Fluorescence

Compound[a]	$k_f{}^b$ (sec^{-1})	k_p (sec^{-1})
Benzene	2×10^6	0.035
Naphthalene	1×10^6	0.044
Quinoline	10×10^6	0.15
Bromobenzene	3×10^6	20
Acetophenone	0.4×10^6	76
Benzophenone	1×10^6	160
1-Iodonaphthalene	2×10^6	350

[a] Data taken from N. J. Turro, *Molecular Photochemistry*, p. 75, W. A. Benjamin, Inc., New York, 1965.

[b] Although these numbers were not taken from gas phase studies, the orders of magnitude and the trends should be reasonably well preserved.

It is possible to measure the speed with which the intermediate free radical forms and decays. The chemical process is not as simple as a phosphorescent process since chemical bonds are being made and broken. Formation of the intermediate radical and decay to new products require complete reshuffling of energy among rotational, vibrational, and electronic forms, with the additional possibility that some energy may also be absorbed or evolved in the form of heat (translational energy). An interesting question to pose in this connection is the problem of the source of the heat of a reaction, that is, has it come from mainly internal sources, or from the relative kinetic energy differences between reactants and products? Questions like this can sometimes be answered after a detailed examination of the results from molecular beam experiments.

The multiplicity of pathways which can occur is well illustrated by the reaction between oxygen atoms and alkenes in the gas phase. A complex mixture of products is obtained which results from competing rearrangement and fragmentation of the transient energy-rich intermediate. The proportion of addition to fragmentation products depends on the total pressure of the system. The pressures at which efficient removal of the excess energy from the unstable intermediate by collisions will occur depend on the lifetimes of the excited products with respect to their fragmentation. Table 6–2 gives some typical lifetimes for excited addition products. These data indicate that at low pressures (0–100 torr) it should be difficult to observe

TABLE 6–2

Lifetimes of Excited Addition Products

Alkene	*Excited product*	*Lifetime* $(sec^{-1})^a$
Ethylene (CH_2=CH_2)	Ethylene oxide (CH_2——CH_2) with O bridge	~10^{-10}
Butadiene (CH_2=$CHCH$=CH_2)	3-Butenal (CH_2=$CHCH_2CH$=O)	1.4×10^{-9}
Butadiene (CH_2=$CHCH$=CH_2)	Butadiene monoxide (CH_2=$CHCH$——CH_2) with O bridge	2.7×10^{-9}
Propylene (CH_3CH=CH_2)	Propylene oxide (CH_3CH——CH_2) with O bridge	5.8×10^{-9}
Propylene (CH_3CH=CH_2)	Propionaldehyde (CH_3CH_2CH=O)	8.0×10^{-9}
Isobutene (($CH_3)_2C$=CH_2)	Isobutyraldehyde (($CH_3)_2CHCH$=O)	~1.5×10^{-7}
1-Butene (CH_3CH_2CH=CH_2)	1-Butene oxide (CH_3CH_2CH——CH) with O bridge	~3×10^{-7}

^{a} Data taken from R. J. Cvetanovic in W. A. Noyes, Jr., G. S. Hammond, and J. N. Pitts, Jr. (eds.), *Advances in Photochemistry*, Vol. 1, p. 125, Interscience, New York, 1963.

stabilized *addition* products in the cases of ethylene and butadiene; isobutene and 1-butene should be more favorable in this respect.

If two species collide, but do not react, there may be a transfer of energy from one to the other. The recipient may decay, by transferring energy to other molecules or by emission of light, or it may use the excess energy to consummate a chemical change. The isomerization of cyclopropane to propylene must follow such a path:

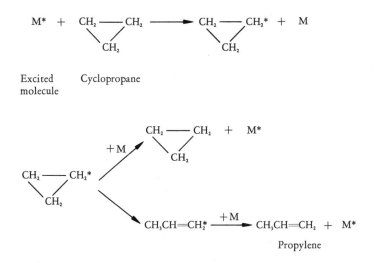

Excited   Cyclopropane
molecule

This example illustrates an important feature of chemical dynamics. Propylene is actually more stable than cyclopropane. However, cyclopropane does not decay smoothly to propylene at low temperatures. At high temperatures reaction occurs, so we can presume that excited forms of cyclopropane can change into excited forms of propylene which in turn are stabilized by transfer of their excess energy to other molecules in the system. We can guess that the "activated" cyclopropane molecule occasionally concentrates enough energy in vibrations that stretch one of the carbon-carbon bonds to lead to rupture.

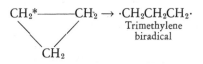

TABLE 6-3

Deactivation of Molecules from the First Excited Vibrational Level to the Vibrational Ground State[a]

Molecule being deactivated	Colliding partner	Temperature °C	Number of collisions
O_2	O_2	15	2.1×10^7
Cl_2	Cl_2	15	3.4×10^4
N_2O	N_2O	25	7.5×10^3
	Ar	25	3.3×10^4
	H_2O	25	1.05×10^2
SCO	SCO	20	1.77×10^4
	H_2	20	2.0×10^2
Ethane (CH_3—CH_3)	Ethane	25	20–74
Propane (CH_3—CH_2—CH_3)	Propane	25	5
Neopentane CH_3 $\mid$ CH_3—C—CH_3 $\mid$ CH_3	Neopentane	25	<2
Methyl fluoride (CH_3F)	Methyl fluoride	19	4.8×10^3

[a] Data taken from J. E. Leffler and E. Grunwald, *Rates and Equilibria of Organic Reactions*, p. 96, John Wiley, New York, 1963.

Migration of a hydrogen atom from the central carbon atom to one of the terminal carbon atoms would produce an excited form of propylene

$$\underset{\cdot CH_2CHCH_2\cdot}{\overset{H}{\mid}} \rightarrow H_3C=CHCH_2^*$$

Even the initial process of activation may itself be complex. A qualitative theory developed by Landau and Teller suggests, for example, that conversion of vibrational energy to translational energy, or the reverse, during collisions should be much more probable for polyatomic molecules than for diatomic molecules. Measurements have been made of the rates at which vibrationally excited molecules are deactivated in collisions. The vibrational energy lost is converted to translational energy. Table 6-3 gives the average number of collisions required to remove the vibrational energy from various molecules in the $v = 1$ states (see Figure 6-3).

6-3 REACTIONS IN LIQUID SOLUTIONS

Many of the concepts pertaining to the dynamics of reactions in the gas phase are also applicable to reactions in condensed phases. The speeds with which such reactions occur are expressed by mathe-

TABLE 6-4

Energy Parameters for Some Equilibria in Solution
and in the Gas Phase

Reaction[a]	Medium	$\Delta \tilde{H}^\circ$ kcal mole^{-1}	$\Delta \tilde{G}^\circ$ kcal mole^{-1}	$\Delta \tilde{S}^\circ$ eu
$I_2 + Cl_2 \rightleftharpoons 2ICl$	Gas	−6.56	−7.37	2.7
	CCl$_4$ sol	−7.94	−8.04	0.4
$I_2 + Br_2 \rightleftharpoons 2IBr$	Gas	−2.74	−3.44	3.1
	CCl$_4$ sol	−3.26	−3.36	1.1
$Br_2 + Cl_2 \rightleftharpoons 2BrCl$	Gas	−0.60	−1.26	2.3
	CCl$_4$ sol	−0.76	−0.71	−0.1

[a] Data taken from C. M. Blair and D. M. Yost, *J. Am. Chem. Soc.*, **55**, 4489 (1933). In contrast, the standard enthalpy change for the dimerization of the very polar molecule acetic acid is −15.3 kcal mole^{-1} in the gas phase, but only −9.7 kcal mole^{-1} in benzene solution.

matical laws similar to those for gas phase reactions, reflecting the fact that the rates in both cases are related to the rates of encounters between reactants and are governed by similar energetic and configurational constraints. Indeed, for certain simple reactions, notably those involving relatively nonpolar reactants, the speeds of reaction and the energetic parameters in various solvents are remarkably close to those in the gas phase. This point is illustrated by data obtained from a study of the equilibria between the halogens in the gaseous state and in carbon tetrachloride solution. The data in Table 6–4 show that $\Delta \tilde{H}°$ and $\Delta \tilde{G}°$ do not vary significantly in going from the gas phase to the liquid phase.

Nevertheless, there are important differences between the dynamics in the gas and liquid phases. In some ways solution re-reactions are simpler! The usefulness of the reaction cross section is no longer as apparent since now the reagent molecules approach each other surrounded by a sheath of solvent molecules. The solvent may influence the course of a reaction in solution in many ways.

Solvation of the Participants in the Reaction, Including the Intermediates

The term solvation, as it is commonly used, is actually vague because of our ignorance of the detailed structure of liquids. In a general sense solvation refers to any binding of solvent molecules with solute molecules, without necessarily specifying the nature of the interaction. Consider a general bimolecular reaction in solution represented by

$$A + B \rightleftharpoons C + D$$

A more detailed description of this process includes at least three steps:

$$A + B \rightleftharpoons (A....B) \rightleftharpoons (C....D) \rightleftharpoons C + D$$

where $(A....B)$ and $(C....D)$ denote the reactant and product *collision complexes*. These complexes may be slightly polarized since electrons are being shuffled about; they will therefore tend to interact with solvent molecules, particularly polar ones, through electrostatic interactions. In addition, even if A, B, C, and D are all nonpolar, they will still interact electrostatically with the solvent because of the known tendency of neighboring molecules to polarize each other.

It is plausible to expect that some of the difference between gas and liquid phase reaction energetics is attributable to varying degrees of solvation of the different species. In the case where all species, including the solvent, are polar, there are several different modes of electrostatic interaction between two species; the potential energy of interaction varies differently with the distance of separation R as follows:

charge-charge	R^{-1}
charge-dipole	R^{-2}
charge-quadrupole	R^{-3}
dipole-dipole	R^{-3}
dipole-quadrupole	R^{-4}
quadrupole-quadrupole	R^{-5}
induced dipole-induced dipole	R^{-6}
induced dipole-induced quadrupole	R^{-8}
induced quadrupole-induced quadrupole	R^{-10}

In many instances it is not clear whether solvation should be described in terms of simple, electrostatic interactions or in terms of the formation of weak covalent bonds.

The occurrence of separated, chemically stable ionic species under ordinary conditions is essentially confined to solvents of high dielectric constant (such as water, which has a dielectric constant of about 80 at room temperature), and it is only in such media that similarly charged ions can easily approach each other to within normal reacting distances. This may be illustrated by simple electron transfer reactions. The asterisks indicate that the reaction is monitored using a radioactive isotope of iron

$$Fe(H_2O)_6^{2+} + {}^*Fe(H_2O)_6^{3+} \rightarrow Fe(H_2O)_6^{3+} + {}^*Fe(H_2O)_6^{2+}$$

The energetic parameters obtained for this reaction can be accounted for by assuming that electron transfer can occur if the reactant ions approach each other closely enough to make the distance between the two iron atoms about 7 Å. At this distance the electrostatic repulsion energy is estimated to be about 4 kcal mole^{-1}. In the gas phase the corresponding repulsion energy for comparable approach would amount to over 250 kcal mole^{-1} (as the student can easily show).

The Cage Effect

The discussion in Section 6–2 of the number of collisions needed to deactivate excited molecules in the gas phase suggests that the duration of an *encounter* between two gaseous molecules is very short. Thus, following a collision between them, two molecules are likely to separate and the probability of two or more successive collisions between the same pair of molecules is small.

In condensed media, however, a pair of ions or molecules which diffuse together are constrained from separating by the *cage effect* exerted by the surrounding molecules, and they generally stay together as nearest neighbors for a relatively long time. In a liquid such as water the duration of this cage lifetime for a pair of molecules is of the order of 10^{-11} to 10^{-10} sec, during which they may undergo between ten and several hundred collisions with each other. For reactions which tend to occur at nearly every collision between reactants, the speed of the reaction closely approaches the upper limit for the rate of diffusional *encounters* between reactants. This upper limit can be estimated from the Smoluchowski–Debye equation:

$$\text{Rate of collision} = \frac{4\pi r_{AB} D_{AB} N}{1000} \left[\frac{W}{e^W - 1} \right] [A][B]$$

where

$$W = \frac{Z_A Z_B e^2}{k T r_{AB} \epsilon}$$

and

r_{AB} is the separation of closest approach of A and B
D_{AB} is the mean diffusion coefficient of A and B
N is Avogadro's number
$Z_A e$ and $Z_B e$ are electrical charges on the reactants
k is Boltzmann's constant
ϵ is the bulk dielectric constant of the solvent.

TABLE 6-5

Rate Constants for Some Diffusion-Controlled Reactions

Reaction (in aqueous solution)	k (liters mole^{-1} sec^{-1})
$H_3O^+ + OH^- \longrightarrow 2H_2O$	1.4×10^{11} [a]
$H_3O^+ + CH_3CO_2^- \longrightarrow CH_3COOH + H_2O$	4.5×10^{10} [a]
$H_3O^+ + NH_3 \longrightarrow NH_4^+ + H_2O$	4.3×10^{10} [a]
$NH_4^+ + {}^-OH \longrightarrow NH_3 + H_2O$	3.4×10^{10} [a]
$Cu^{2+} + e^- \longrightarrow Cu^+$	3.3×10^{10} [b]
$O_2 + e^- \longrightarrow O_2^-$	1.9×10^{10} [b]
$\cdot OH + I^- \longrightarrow OH^- + I\cdot$	1.0×10^{10} [c]
$Fe(CN)_6^{3-} + e^- \longrightarrow Fe(CN)_6^{4-}$	3.0×10^{9} [b]

[a] M. Eigen, Angew. Chem. (Intern. Ed.), **3**, 1 (1964).
[b] E. J. Hart, Science, **146**, 19 (1964).
[c] J. K. Thomas, Trans. Faraday Soc., **61**, 702 (1965).

The rate constants for bimolecular reactions are defined by the following rate law:

$$\text{Rate per unit concentration} = k[A][B]$$

The rate constant k is usually expressed in units of liters mole^{-1} sec^{-1}. If a reaction occurs on every encounter between A and B molecules, it is clear that k will be equal to the encounter rate constant calculated from the Smoluchowski–Debye equation. This rate constant is of the order of 10^{10} liters mole^{-1} sec^{-1} for neutral molecules and somewhat higher or lower for ions depending on whether their charges are opposite or similar. Some "diffusion-controlled" reactions are listed below in Table 6–5, along with measured values of their speeds.

Participation of the Solvent in the Reaction

Many examples could be cited where the solvent plays an important participating role in the reaction. In the case of the substitution reaction,

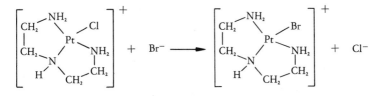

$H_2NCH_2CH_2NHCH_2CH_2NH_2$ = diethylenetriamine = dien

the mathematical law experimentally obtained for the speed of the reaction in aqueous solution clearly shows that the product is arising by two independent paths.   One is direct displacement of Cl^- by Br^-, whereas the other is generally accepted to be the following:

$$Pt(dien)Cl^+ + H_2O \rightleftharpoons Pt(dien)(H_2O)^{2+} + Cl^-$$
$$Pt(dien)(H_2O)^{2+} + Br^- \rightleftharpoons Pt(dien)Br^+ + H_2O$$

If the solvent can accept and/or donate protons, then proton transfer reactions can be expected to proceed through the intermediacy of one or more protonated or deprotonated solvent molecules.   Thus, in aqueous solution the reaction

$$(CH_3)_3NH^+ + (CH_3)_3N^* \rightleftharpoons (CH_3)_3N + (CH_3)_3\overset{*}{N}H^+$$

probably proceeds through one or more intervening water molecules as illustrated:

$$(CH_3)_3N^+ \!\!-\!\! \text{(H)} \mathbin{\overset{\frown}{-\!-\!-}} O \!-\!\! \text{(H)} \mathbin{\overset{\frown}{-\!-\!-}} \overset{*}{N}(CH_3)_3 \longrightarrow (CH_3)_3N + O \begin{smallmatrix} H \\ \diagup \\ \diagdown \\ H \end{smallmatrix} + \left[(CH_3)_3N^{*}H\right]^+$$

Such processes are probably associated with observed autoionization phenomena in water and other protonic solvents.

In this section and in Section 6–2 we have presented qualitative reasoning to show that the path followed by a reaction in solution will be modified by comparison with reaction processes in the gas phase.   With these ideas as a background, we shall examine in the next several chapters the details of some chemistry carried out in condensed media.

EXERCISES

1. Define or describe clearly the following important terms and concepts: cage effect, collision, collision complex, decay, dielectric constant, diffusion-controlled reaction, dipole-dipole interaction, encounter, fluorescence, lifetime of an excited species, molecular beam experiment, phosphorescence, rate constant, reaction cross section, solvation, threshold energy, vibrational energy level.

2. An estimate of the difference between intermolecular distances in the gas phase and in the liquid phase can be obtained by comparing the molar volumes of a material in the liquid state and in the gaseous state at a given temperature. Estimate how much farther apart the water molecules will be in steam at 100° C than in liquid water at 100° C.

3. According to the kinetic molecular theory the kinetic energy of a molecule is equally partitioned among its translational degrees of freedom, each degree of freedom possessing energy $\frac{1}{2}kT$ per molecule.

(a) Calculate the velocity of a methyl radical at 25° C, assuming all molecules in the sample to have the same velocity.

(b) Using the implication in the text that the collision cross section can be regarded as the area of a B molecule which is presented to an approaching A molecule, calculate the collision cross section for a methyl radical encountering another methyl radical. Assume a methyl radical to behave like a hard sphere whose radius is the length of a carbon-hydrogen bond (1.08 Å).

(c) Finally, calculate the rate per unit reactant concentration for the recombination of methyl radicals. It is necessary to assume something about the *relative* velocities of the colliding molecules; assume this velocity is twice the velocity calculated in part (a). Compare your answer with the experimental value of 3.1×10^{13} cm³ mole⁻¹ sec⁻¹ obtained by Kistiakowsky and Roberts.

4. This problem is really a library research project. As intimated in the text, many elementary processes are fast enough to make it necessary to apply special methods in estimating how fast they occur. If a system does indeed react by a single-step process and is only slightly displaced from equilibrium, it will return to equilibrium (relax) according to a very simple mathematical law. One technique for measuring rapid equilibria is to observe the relaxation of a system which has been slightly altered due to a change in one of the variables that describe the state of the system.

In the list below are the names of several methods used for studying rapid equilibria. Columns 2 and 3, which do not correspond to the entries in column 1, indicate the kind of imposition placed on the system and the manner in which the relaxation is measured. Go to the literature and read briefly about each of these methods. Then match columns 2 and 3 with the appropriate entries in column 1. Write a short paragraph or two describing the essence of each method.

Method	*Imposition*	*Detection or measurement*
Temperature jump	Pulsed vibrational excitation	Periodic fluctuation of pressure
Flash photolysis	Molecular kinetic energy of translation and rotation	Density gradients
Spectrophone	New, vibrationally excited species	Infrared emission or vibrational fine structure
Dielectric relaxation	Thermal excitation	Conductivity or optical absorption
Shock	Mechanical agitation	Sound velocity and absorption
Dissociation field	Electronic excitation	Emission spectrum
Ultrasonics	Rotational orientation	Dielectric constant or loss
Chemical	Electrical charge	Conductivity

5. Why should you expect, in general, that vibrational deactivation of a substance should be slower than its rotational deactivation? Note that the quanta of translational energy are much smaller than either rotational or vibrational quanta.

6. Excited calcium atoms phosphoresce at 6537 Å. In what part of the electromagnetic spectrum is this? How much energy, in kilocalories, does 1 g-atom of excited calcium atoms lose during the process?

7. Consider, successively, the following situation:
(a) a sodium ion is located 5 Å away from a bromide ion in a solvent of bulk dielectric constant 80;
(b) a sodium ion is located 5 Å away from the center of a hydrogen bromide dipole in a solvent of bulk dielectric constant 80,

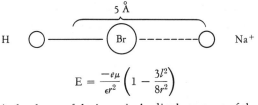

$$E = \frac{-e\mu}{\epsilon r^2}\left(1 - \frac{3l^2}{8r^2}\right)$$

where e is the charge of the ion, μ is the dipole moment of the dipole, r is the collinear distance of the ion from the dipole, l is the length of the dipole, and ϵ is the solvent dielectric constant;

(c) a sodium ion is located 5 Å away from a bromine molecule in a solvent of dielectric constant 80,

$$PE = \frac{-\alpha e^2}{2r^4\epsilon^2}$$

where α is the polarizability of the nonpolar molecule.

To get an idea of the relative magnitudes of the different electrostatic interactions, calculate the energy of the charge-charge interaction in part (a), the energy of the charge-dipole interaction in part (b), and the energy of the charge-induced dipole interaction in part (c). Hydrogen bromide has a dipole moment of 0.802 debye and a bond length of 1.42 Å; bromine has a polarizability of 6.43 Å³ molecule⁻¹.

8. An approximate expression for the diffusion coefficient of a spherical body of radius r in a medium of viscosity η was derived by Einstein:

$$D = \frac{kT}{6\pi\eta r}$$

Use the Smoluchowski–Debye equation to estimate the velocity of combination of the hydronium ion and the hydroxide ion in water, and compare with the experimental value in Table 6-5.

VII

An Illustrative Chemical Reaction

7-1 THE IODIDE-HYPOCHLORITE REACTION

Since most processes of interest to the chemist are carried out in
solution, let us now consider an example of such a process that is
a classic for its superficial simplicity. The illustration chosen is the
reaction in aqueous alkaline medium between iodide ion and hypochlorite ion.

$$I^-(aq) + OCl^-(aq) \rightarrow OI^-(aq) + Cl^-(aq)$$

The reader should immediately ask two questions at this point:

(1) How is the reaction monitored experimentally?
(2) How are the results conveniently expressed?

The answer to the second question is of general use to experimen-
talists. Results are expressed by a reaction rate equation, and it is
customary to describe the reaction rate as the change in concentration of a reactant or product per unit time. Change in concentrations
rather than actual numbers of moles is desired because experience
has told us that rates generally do not depend upon the size of the
sample involved. Therefore, the *intensive* quantity "concentration"
is clearly appropriate. The above reaction may then be described
by an equation of the following form:

Rate = k multiplied by some function of the concentrations   (7-1)

where k is a constant referred to as a rate constant.

The answer to the first question posed above is not so easy. Methods of following reactions can be placed in one of two classes: destructive or nondestructive. By the former we mean that the reaction is followed by observing the disappearance of a particular reactant or the appearance of a particular product by its reaction with a given analytical reagent that will not react with any other component of the system. Thus, if we have the type reaction

$$A + B \rightarrow C + D$$

we could follow this by withdrawing samples of the reaction mixture at intervals and carrying out the reaction

$$C + X \rightarrow Y$$

It is necessary that X not react significantly with A, B, and D. Destructive methods of monitoring may not always be foolproof because in some instances it could be that the method of analysis would significantly affect the rate being measured.

If destructive methods interfere one hunts for a convenient nondestructive means of analysis. Electrical conductivity and spectroscopy are potential candidates for following many reactions. The reaction between I^- and OCl^- has been followed by spectroscopic means because at the blue end of the visible spectrum (near 400 millimicrons) hypoiodite ions absorb light, whereas hypochlorite, iodide, and chloride ions are essentially transparent. Thus, the reaction may conveniently be monitored by observing the appearance of light absorption at 400 millimicrons.

The results of spectroscopic analysis of the hypochlorite reaction in 1.0 molar NaOH lead to the experimental rate equation

$$\frac{d[OI^-]}{dt} = k[I^-][OCl^-] \qquad (7-2)$$

where $d[OI^-]/dt$ means the time-rate of appearance of hypoiodite ion. Notice that Equation (7-2) does not contain a term in $[OH^-]$ even though the presence of hydroxide is very important to the reaction course. The stoichiometry of the reaction does not assign a role to hydroxide, but if the concentration of OH^- were important we would not be able to ascertain this by making measurements at only a single OH^- concentration, particularly if the latter were in great excess. We shall return to this point later. It should also be pointed out that the following equality also holds for the hypochlorite reaction:

$$\frac{d[OI^-]}{dt} = \frac{-d[OCl^-]}{dt} \tag{7-3}$$

but this equation is merely a check on the stoichiometry of the reaction, and in general, it is not safe to write analogous equations for other reactions being studied unless the stoichiometry is well established or unless the two necessary independent measures are made.

We would like, however, to rewrite Equation (7–2) in terms of quantities other than concentrations, in order to express the experimental results in the language of thermodynamics. Making the rough approximation that concentrations are equal to activities, we have

$$\mu_X = \tilde{G}_X{}^\circ + RT \ln[X^-] \tag{7-4}$$

and therefore

$$[X^-] = \exp\left[\frac{(\mu_X - \tilde{G}_X{}^\circ)}{RT}\right] \tag{7-5}$$

Equation (7–2) can then be rewritten as

$$\frac{d[OI^-]}{dt} = k \exp\left[\frac{(\tilde{G}^\circ{}_{I^-} + \tilde{G}^\circ{}_{OCl^-} - \mu_{I^-} - \mu_{OCl-})}{RT}\right] \tag{7-6}$$

This equation is actually no more convenient than Equation (7–2), but it has the important advantage that it predicts a form of the dependence of reaction rate on temperature which was first discovered empirically by Arrhenius.

7–2 INTERPRETATION OF THE RATE CONSTANT

At this point it is clearly desirable to know something more about the rate constant k. The hypochlorite reaction is considered to be slow because it can be monitored by simple analytical procedures at room temperature. This means that somewhere in our reaction network there is a point of narrowest constriction that must be slowing down the process. This point of narrowest constriction is called the *rate-determining step*. Any number of naïve reasons could be thought of to explain the slowness of the reaction. An important additional experimental observation must now be included. If we run the experiment several times, keeping $[I^-]_0$ and $[OCl^-]_0$ constant for each run but varying the concentration of hydroxide ion, then it turns out that the rate law can be satisfactorily represented by the equation

$$\frac{d[IO^-]}{dt} = \frac{k'[I^-][OCl^-]}{[OH^-]} \qquad (7\text{--}7)$$

This is in no way contradictory to Equation (7–2) if we set

$$k = \frac{k'}{[OH^-]} \qquad (7\text{--}8)$$

We should like to explain this inverse dependence on hydroxide concentration. Apparently, the reaction between iodide and hypochlorite proceeds faster in the presence of less OH^- which, as far as the stoichiometry is concerned, is not even there. Since the reaction is conducted in aqueous medium, and since we know that as hydroxide ion concentration increases, hydronium ion (H_3O^+) concentration decreases, perhaps a reasonable explanation is that the reaction is *acid catalyzed*. Something similar to this has been proposed as a candidate mechanism. In aqueous solution OCl^- hydrolyzes to a slight extent according to the equation

$$OCl^-(aq) + H_2O \rightleftharpoons HOCl(aq) + OH^-(aq) \qquad K_1 = 2.9 \times 10^{-7}$$

Thus, only a very small fraction of hypochlorite will be present as the neutral acid. However, if there is any substance at all to the simple idea that two negatively charged species ought to react much slower with each other than should a negative species with a neutral species, then hypochlorous acid can be reasonably expected to react with iodide ion.

$$I^-(aq) + HOCl(aq) \xrightarrow{k''} HOI(aq) + Cl^-(aq) \quad \text{slow}$$

This accounts for one of the observed products; in order to account for the formation of OI^-, we note that HOI, a weak acid, should be rapidly equilibrated with hypoiodite ion

$$OH^-(aq) + HOI(aq) \rightleftharpoons H_2O + OI^-(aq) \quad K_2 \approx 10^3$$

We are now in a position to see if these ideas can account for the form of Equation (7-7). Since K_2 is large it follows that the rate of appearance of OI^- will be essentially equal to the rate of appearance of its conjugate acid (HOI). From above we have

$$\frac{d[HOI]}{dt} = k''[I^-][HOCl] \tag{7-9}$$

However, from the hydrolysis of OCl^- we also know that

$$[HOCl] = \frac{K_1[OCl^-]}{[OH^-]} \tag{7-10}$$

Substituting this into Equation (7-9) gives

$$\frac{d[HOI]}{dt} = \frac{k''K_1[I^-][OCl^-]}{[OH^-]}$$
$$= \frac{d[OI^-]}{dt} \tag{7-11}$$

by hypothesis. This is identical to Equation (7-7) where $k' = k''K_1$.

Our surprising conclusion is that even though only a small amount of OCl^- is present in the form of HOCl, apparently placing a proton on the oxygen tremendously encourages reaction. This tells us that whatever happens to hypochlorous acid does not happen to hypochlorite ion. We surmise that this is some kind of electronic effect, since the function of the proton is to draw electronic charge away from the oxygen atom. We shall continue our study of this reaction in the next chapter.

EXERCISES

1. Suggest ways of monitoring the progress of the following reactions:

(a) $2KClO_3(s) \xrightarrow{\Delta} 2KCl(s) + 3O_2(g)$

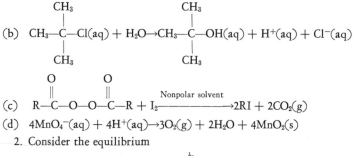

(b) CH_3—C—Cl(aq) + H_2O→CH_3—C—OH(aq) + H^+(aq) + Cl^-(aq)

(c)   R—C—O—O—C—R + I_2 $\xrightarrow{\text{Nonpolar solvent}}$ 2RI + $2CO_2$(g)

(d) $4MnO_4^-$(aq) + $4H^+$(aq)→$3O_2$(g) + $2H_2O$ + $4MnO_2$(s)

2. Consider the equilibrium

$$A + B \underset{k_{-1}}{\overset{k_1}{\rightleftharpoons}} C + D$$

(a) Show that the well-known relationship between the equilibrium constant and the standard free energy change of the reaction may be derived by assuming that equilibrium means the rates in both directions are equal.

(b) The results from above suggest that the rate constant k_1, for example, should be of the form

$$k_1 = M \exp\left(-\frac{\Delta E_1}{RT}\right)$$

where M is a constant, independent of temperature, and ΔE_1 is an energy term which is a function of the nature of the reactants. In other words,

$$\Delta E_1 - \Delta E_{-1} = \Delta \tilde{G}°$$

The term ΔE_1 is also supposed to be temperature independent; it is called the activation energy for the reaction. What sort of graphical method would you employ to show that, in practice, M and ΔE_1 are essentially constant for a particular reaction?

(c) Recalling that $\Delta G = \Delta H - T\Delta S$, what fundamental thermodynamic quantity is M, the preexponential factor, a function of?

3. What must be the units of a rate constant for a rate law of the form

$$-\frac{d[A]}{dt} = k[A][B]$$

4. If a reaction takes place in more than one step, is it correct to say that the rate of the reaction is essentially equal to the rate of the slowest step? Is it correct to say that the overall rate constant for the reaction is equal to the rate constant for the rate-determining step?

VIII

Mechanisms and Rate Laws

8-1 THE RATE-DETERMINING STEP

In studying the reaction between iodide ion and hypochlorite ion, we have been led to the following rate law:

$$\frac{d[\text{IO}^-]}{dt} = \frac{k[\text{I}^-][\text{OCl}^-]}{[\text{OH}^-]} \tag{8-1}$$

Even though OH^- does not actually appear in the overall balanced equation, it appears in the denominator of the rate expression because the reaction is carried out in aqueous basic medium where the following equilibrium is established

$$\text{OCl}^-(\text{aq}) + \text{H}_2\text{O} \overset{K}{\rightleftharpoons} \text{HOCl}(\text{aq}) + \text{OH}^-(\text{aq})$$

We might actually worry about the justification for writing this equation as a rapidly reversible process rather than considering the rates of the forward and reverse reactions. The answer to this is that a body of common experience shows that rate constants of proton transfer from oxygen to oxygen (see p. 60) or from nitrogen to oxygen are usually much too large to be measured by conventional techniques. Thus, since we know that the reaction between I^- and OCl^- can be conventionally measured, we presume that equilibration between hypochlorous acid and hypochlorite ion is not the rate-determining factor.

[71]

A candidate for the mechanism of the reaction can now be formulated. As the rate-determining step we suppose that iodide ion reacts with hypochlorous acid.

$$I^-(aq) + HOCl(aq) \xrightarrow{k_2} HOI(aq) + Cl^-(aq)$$

The procedure is then to formulate the rate law on the basis of the candidate mechanism. This part of the game is purely mathematical, and so there is no chance of writing down an incorrect candidate rate law; the rate law follows automatically from the equations written in the mechanism. If the derived rate law does not fit the form of the experimental rate law, then our mechanism must be rejected.

The rate for formation of HOI above is the rate at which the above reaction occurs. Using Equation (8–1) we may write:

$$\frac{d[HOI]}{dt} = k_2[I^-][HOCl]$$

$$= \frac{k_2 K[I^-][OCl^-]}{[OH^-]} \simeq \frac{k_2 K[I^-]T_{ClO}^-}{[OH^-]}$$

$$T_{ClO}^- = \text{Total hypochlorite} = [HOCl] + [OCl^-] \quad (8\text{–}2)$$

As usual, water is not included in the final rate law if we assume that the molar concentration of water is absorbed in the constant K. The $[OCl^-]$ term in Equation (8–1) is almost equal to the total hypochlorite concentration because only a tiny fraction of the total is converted to the reactive hypochlorous acid under the conditions of the experiments. The experimental data used to establish the rate law were actually expressed in terms of T_{ClO}^- so Equations (8–1) and (8–2) have the same form, and hence we do have a candidate mechanism.

8–2   AN ALTERNATIVE MECHANISM

Suppose we consider another possible mechanism:

$$I^-(aq) + H_2O \underset{}{\overset{K'}{\rightleftharpoons}} HI(aq) + OH^-(aq)$$
$$OCl^-(aq) + HI(aq) \underset{}{\overset{k_2'}{\rightleftharpoons}} HOI(aq) + Cl^-(aq)$$

The rate law to be obtained from this mechanism is:

$$\frac{d[Cl^-]}{dt} = \frac{d[HOI]}{dt} = k_2'[OCl^-][HI]$$

$$= \frac{k_2'K'[OCl^-][I^-]}{[OH^-]} \cong \frac{k_2'K'[OCl^-]T_{I^-}}{[OH^-]} \quad (8\text{-}3)$$

Comparison with Equation (8-2) shows that both rate laws have the same form; this means that both mechanisms are potential candidates. We must conclude from this that kinetics can never completely establish a mechanism, but can only serve to indicate whether a particular mechanism is a possibility or not.

An additional comment can be made. The rate-determining step for the second mechanism might also have been written as

$$OCl^-(aq) + HI(aq) \xrightarrow{k_3} OI^-(aq) + HCl(aq)$$

Here we have formation of OI^- rather than the free acid HOI. Our kinetic data, however, cannot tell us which is correct because experience would suggest that OI^- and HOI equilibrate very rapidly. This is a kinetic ambiguity, then, and to decide between the two choices we must do other types of experiments or employ reasoning drawn from structural theory.

We might ask why Cl^- does not appear in the rate law; naïvely, it might be expected that addition of excess Cl^- to the system should slow down the rate. The reason why Cl^- is not included in the rate law is that the law is written for the early stages of the reaction where the system is far from equilibrium; thus the rate is determined essentially by initial conditions (concentrations of reactants). The back reaction is presumed to be unimportant. Expressed in terms of chemical potentials, we mean

$$\sum \mu_{reac} \gg \sum \mu_{prod} \quad (8\text{-}4)$$

8-3 A FURTHER LOOK AT THE FIRST MECHANISM

Looking at the first mechanism in closer detail, we might inquire whether it is reasonable. In this mechanism iodine forms a bond to an oxygen to displace Cl^-. Is there any analogy for this sort of behavior? Hydrogen peroxide reacts rapidly with iodide ion as shown below:

$$HO-OH(aq) + I^-(aq) \rightarrow OH^-(aq) + HOI(aq)$$
$$\updownarrow$$
$$H_2O + OI^-(aq)$$

If we replace the hydrogens with organic alkyl groups, we can still effect reaction of iodide ion with the resulting dialkyl peroxide, although the reaction is slower:

$$RO-OR + I^- \rightarrow OR^- + ROI$$
$$\downarrow \ + HI$$
$$ROH + I_2$$

By looking at several such examples we can build up a set of consistent data which lead to the conclusion that reactions between I^- and covalently bound oxygen proceed fairly readily. It looks as if the other parts of the molecules do not play the *major* role in the reaction.

This statement, however, should not be and is not true when we compare reactants of different *charge*, on inspection of the following two reactions:

$$I^-(aq) + OCl^-(aq) \xrightarrow{k_2''} IO^-(aq) + Cl^-(aq)$$
$$I^-(aq) + HOCl(aq) \xrightarrow{k_2} HOI(aq) + Cl^-(aq)$$

Apparently $k_2 \gg k_2''$, if we presume we are talking about the right mechanism. The inequality follows from the fact that the first equation would not give the experimentally observed rate law. Hence, even though hypochlorite ion concentration is much greater than that of the free acid, it is apparently the latter which reacts with iodide ion; in other words, knowing the correct mechanism gives us the exceedingly interesting piece of information that $HOCl$ is much more reactive toward I^- than OCl^- is. We ask, then, why is it easier to displace Cl^- from oxygen when there is also a proton attached?

One answer which we might submit is that reaction with OCl^- involves the interaction of two species bearing like charges, and on a purely electrostatic basis this would not be as preferable as the second reaction. A more general way of looking at this is from an electronic

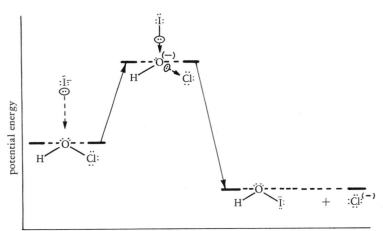

FIGURE 8-1   Model for the mechanism of the reaction
between hypochlorous acid and iodide ion.

structural viewpoint. From the model shown in Figure 8–1, the oxygen in OCl⁻ has three nonbonding pairs of electrons; at some intermediate stage (called the "transition state") in the reaction of I⁻
with OCl⁻, it looks as if we are trying to force ten electrons into the
valence shell of oxygen. By putting a proton on oxygen we gain
some relief from the stress on the system arising from electron-
electron repulsion. A structural model of the reaction pathway is
shown in Figure 8–1.

EXERCISES

1. Why do you suppose that proton-transfer steps can rarely be the rate-
determining steps of reactions?

2. (a) Consider the system

$$A \overset{k_1}{\rightleftharpoons} B \qquad \text{Rapid}$$

$$B \overset{k_2}{\rightleftharpoons} C \qquad \text{Slow}$$

and write an expression for the rate of the reaction in terms of the concentration of A.

(b) Formulate an expression for the *net* rate for formation of species B.

(c) In some systems B is a reactive intermediate which reacts to give a product almost as soon as it is formed, that is, its concentration never builds up to a detectable level as time passes. This is the so-called *steady state* assumption. The mathematical statement of the steady state assumption is:

$$\text{Rate of formation of B} \cong \text{Rate of disappearance of B}$$

Using this assumption and the results of part (b), write an expression for the rate for formation of species C. What inequality will allow you to equate this expression with that from part (a)?

3. Many organic halides can react with solvent (solvolyze) by one of the two extreme mechanisms shown below:

<table>
<tr><td align="center">*Mechanism 1*</td><td align="center">*Mechanism 2*</td></tr>
<tr><td align="center">Slow</td><td align="center">Slow</td></tr>
<tr><td align="center">$RCl \rightleftharpoons R^+ + Cl^-$</td><td align="center">$H_2O + RCl \rightleftharpoons H_2O^+ - R + Cl^-$</td></tr>
<tr><td align="center">Fast</td><td align="center">Fast</td></tr>
<tr><td align="center">$R^+ + H_2O \rightleftharpoons ROH + H^+$</td><td align="center">$H_2O^+ - R + H_2O \rightleftharpoons HOR + H_3O^+$</td></tr>
</table>

Make the steady state assumption and show that for mechanism 1 the rate for formation of acid should be a function of $[Cl^-]$, that is, show that there should be a mass-law effect on the rate.

4. Experiment shows that the rate law for the gas phase reaction

$$2O_3(g) \rightleftharpoons 3O_2(g)$$

has the form $(-d[O_3])/dt = k[O_3]^2/[O_2]$. Suggest a mechanism in accord with this rate law.

5. The *order of a reaction* is defined as the sum of the exponents of the concentration terms in the rate law:

$$\frac{-d[C]}{dt} = k[C]^c[D]^d \cdots \cdots [N]^n$$

$$\text{Order} = c + d + \cdots + n$$

A test to see whether a reaction is first order or not is to measure the time required to reduce the concentration of A to half its initial value

$$A \xrightarrow{k'} B + C$$

Write an expression for this *half-life* τ in terms of the rate constant k'. What is the half-life for a zeroth order reaction?

6. In the mechanism suggested for the iodide-hypochlorite reaction, iodide attacks the oxygen center to displace chloride. Work out another mechanism and its rate law for the possibility where iodide attacks the chlorine center to displace hydroxide. Do you think your mechanism is plausible?

IX

The Interpretation of Rate Equations by Means of the Collision and the Transition State Theories

We have seen previously that the rate law for the reaction between iodide ion and hypochlorite ion in a basic aqueous solution may be written

$$\frac{d[\text{IO}^-]}{dt} = \frac{k[\text{I}^-][\text{ClO}^-]}{[\text{OH}^-]} \qquad (9\text{-}1)$$

or more simply as

$$\frac{d[\text{IO}^-]}{dt} = k'[\text{I}^-][\text{HOCl}] \qquad (9\text{-}2)$$

We now inquire as to a more detailed interpretation of the rate constant k'.

9-1 THE COLLISION THEORY

In the early days of the development of kinetics there arose a theory of bimolecular reactions which was based on the model of collision between two incompressible spheres. A principal tenet of this collision theory, as it was formulated by Trautz and Lewis before 1920, is that in order for a bimolecular reaction to occur, it is necessary for the reacting atoms or molecules to collide. If collision were the only factor necessary to account for the occurrence of a bimolecular reaction, then the expected rate constant should be identical to the collision frequency at unit concentrations of reactants. The rates of collision of molecules in solution can be calculated from the Smoluchowski–Debye equation (p. 59) or from experimentally measured rates of diffusion of solute molecules. The rates can be expressed by a rate constant for bimolecular reaction

$$A + B \xrightarrow{k_{dif}} \underset{\substack{\text{Collision} \\ \text{complex}}}{(AB)}$$

For solvents of normal viscosity at room temperature, and with solute molecules of ordinary sizes, the value of k_{dif} is approximately 10^{10} liters $mole^{-1}$ sec^{-1}. For a solution with $[I^-] = 1$ molar, $[OCl^-] = 1$ molar, and $NaOH = 1$ molar, the concentration of HOCl is 3×10^{-7} molar. We can calculate the rate of encounters between iodide ions and hypochlorous acid molecules:

$$\begin{aligned}
\text{Rate of encounter} &= k_{dif}[I^-][HOCl] \\
&\approx 10^{10} \times 1 \times 3 \times 10^{-7} \text{ moles liter}^{-1} \text{ sec}^{-1} \\
&\approx 3 \times 10^3 \text{ moles liter}^{-1} \text{ sec}^{-1}
\end{aligned}$$

If reaction occurred at every encounter between the reactants, the *initial* rate would be sufficient to produce products at the rate of 3×10^3 moles liter^{-1} sec^{-1}. If reaction continued for as long as a second at this rate, 10^6 times as much product would be produced as there was of the original reactants. This would obviously be a physical impossibility and we realize that the rate would fall very rapidly as the reaction progressed because of the decrease in the concentrations of reactants. However, it is clear that most of the material would be consumed during a period too short to measure by conventional methods. For example, let us calculate the time required to consume half of the starting materials by integrating the rate equation:

$$\frac{d[OI^-]}{dt} = k_{dif}K_1[I^-]T_{OCl^-}$$

$$[I^-]_0 = \text{initial iodide}$$
$$= [T_{OCl^-}]_0 = \text{initial hypochlorite} = 1$$
$$[OI^-] = x$$
$$\frac{dx}{dt} = 3 \times 10^3 (1-x)^2$$

$$\int_{x=0}^{x=0.5} \frac{dx}{(1-x)^2} = \int_{t=0}^{t=t_{1/2}} 3 \times 10^3 \, dt$$

$$\frac{1}{1-x}\Bigg]_{x=0}^{x=0.5} = 3 \times 10^3 \, t_{1/2}$$

$$t_{1/2} = 3.3 \times 10^{-4} \sec \tag{9-3}$$

The observed rate of reaction is *very much slower*, so we conclude that the collisional frequency is far greater than the frequency of collisions that actually lead to reaction!

Early workers realized that not all collisions produce chemical transformation. It was postulated that only those collisions having a certain relative translational energy along the line of centers in excess of some minimum value of E_0 could lead to reaction. To take this into account a Boltzmann factor was therefore included

$$k_{bi} = k_{dif} \exp\left(-\frac{E_0}{RT}\right) \tag{9-4}$$

Unfortunately, this now introduces the additional problem of determining E_0. In general, this was done by measuring the rate at two different temperatures:

$$\frac{k_2}{k_1} = \left[\frac{T_2}{T_1}\right]^{1/2} \times \frac{\exp(-E_0/RT_2)}{\exp(-E_0/RT_1)} \tag{9-5}$$

This equation can then be solved for E_0 and then inserted back into Equation (9-4) for future use. One of the early triumphs of collision theory was the good agreement it gave with the experimental data of Bodenstein for the bimolecular reaction of hydrogen iodide to give hydrogen and iodine.

$$2HI \rightarrow I_2 + H_2$$

Usually, T_1 and T_2 can be measured more accurately than k_1 and k_2, so that if T_1 and T_2 are relatively close, there may be a resulting large error in the value of E_0. This means, then, that collision theory should be much less successful in condensed phases than in the gas phase. In the 1930's there arose a new theory of reaction rates, at first developed by Pelzer and Wigner and later exploited in great detail by Eyring. The transition state theory, as it is called, is the starting point for many discussions of reaction rates.

9–2 THE TRANSITION STATE THEORY

In solution the time of contact between nearest neighbors (an encounter) is on the order of 10^{-10} sec. Exchange of energy among various forms such as vibrations, rotations, and translations, however, takes place in a much shorter span of time, usually 10^{-13} to 10^{-12} sec. Hence, during the time of an encounter a molecule has ample opportunity to exchange energy with other parts of the system. This leads to the *reasonable hypothesis* that in a bimolecular reaction the reacting species form a *transition state* which is in a kind of energetic equilibrium with the environment. The transition state can then decompose to give products.

$$A + B \underset{}{\overset{K^\ddagger}{\rightleftharpoons}} (A \cdots B)^\ddagger \overset{k^\ddagger}{\to} C + D \tag{9–6}$$

Whereas collision theory is based on mechanics, transition state theory makes use of thermodynamic concepts. Essentially, what is done is to assume the existence of a potential energy surface, which is an n-dimensional graph of the potential energy of the system versus the interatomic distances of the interacting species. Except for the very simplest of systems, potential surfaces cannot be easily constructed.

At some configuration of all the nuclei along the path leading to products there will be an area of maximum potential energy. The structure in this configurational region is referred to as the *transition state*. A principal assumption of this theory is that the transition state is in equilibrium with reactants. The justification for this, of course, is the long contact time (at least in condensed phases) between reacting species, which was mentioned earlier.

The rate of reaction is now formulated as the rate of passage through the transition state; in effect, the transition state is the "bottleneck" of the reaction pathway. The usual representation of a reacting system is a two-dimensional slice of the potential energy surface. Since we are not yet in a position to calculate accurately the distribution of various forms of internal energy in molecules, the ordinate of such graphs is denoted as free energy.

In this diagram $\Delta G^{\ddagger}$ is the free energy of activation, analogous but not identical to the E_0 introduced before. The free energy of activation must not be confused with the standard free energy change for the reaction, which involves the difference in standard free energies between reactants and products.

The abscissa of the graph below is a somewhat complicated function of several bond bendings and stretchings, and it is this unstable vibrational degree of freedom which leads to product formation. It is an additional postulate of the theory that nearly all of the

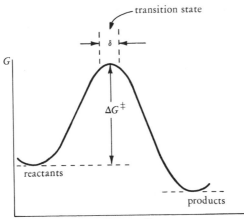

FIGURE 9-1 **Schematic representation of a reaction system.**

transition state molecules which are about to decompose into product were formed from reactant molecules; this fraction (represented by the symbol κ) is close to 1 for many reactions. The unstable vibrational degree of freedom mentioned above appears in the mathematical development of an expression for the rate constant as a multiplicative constant. More precisely, the theory gives as the relevant equation for a bimolecular reaction

$$k_{bi} = \frac{kT}{h} K^{\ddagger} \tag{9-7}$$

where h is Planck's constant, k is Boltzmann's constant, and T is the absolute temperature. The $K^{\ddagger}$ is the equilibrium constant of Equation (9-6), but it should be remembered that this is only a defined and not a true equilibrium constant, since the molecule in a *state of change* cannot be truly at equilibrium (a state of balance) with its environment. Transition state theory can also be applied to unimolecular reactions; an equation similar to (9-7) again applies, although now the quantity $K^{\ddagger}$ will have a different form than in the bimolecular case.

It is important to stress again that the transition state is that state at which the reacting system is clearly becoming product. Notice that Figure 8-1 implies that for thermally controlled reactions (where statistical equilibrium can be reasonably assured), we have the same transitional region for both the forward reaction and the backward reaction

$$A + B \underset{}{\overset{K_1^{\ddagger}}{\rightleftharpoons}} C^{\ddagger} \overset{k_f}{\rightarrow} D + E$$
$$D + E \underset{}{\overset{K_2^{\ddagger}}{\rightleftharpoons}} C^{\ddagger} \overset{k_r}{\rightarrow} A + B \tag{9-8}$$

In the first case A + B and $C^{\ddagger}$ are in pseudoequilibrium, whereas in the second case $C^{\ddagger}$ is decomposing to yield A + B.

EXERCISES

1. If the order of a one-step process is n, what are the units of the rate constant?

2. A general rule of thumb is that increasing the temperature of a reaction

medium by $10°$ C roughly doubles the reaction rate. From collision theory, what does this imply about the approximate magnitude of E_0? Is this reasonable?

3. An important quantity in kinetic-molecular theory is the average distance traversed by a molecule before it collides with another; this distance is the *mean free path*. How would one calculate this for a homogeneous, one-component gaseous sample using collision theory? Arrange the following gases in order of decreasing mean free path: chlorine, helium, carbon dioxide, and nitrogen.

4. The Arrhenius equation introduced earlier (Chapter 7, Exercise 2) may be regarded as a special case of Equation (9-4) in which the temperature dependence of the preexponential factor is not considered. The data given below were obtained by Bodenstein for the reaction

$$2HI \xrightarrow{k} H_2 + I_2$$

Fit these data to an Arrhenius equation and calculate the value of the activation energy and the preexponential factor:

$T(°K)$	k_{obs} (liter mole^{-1} sec^{-1})
556	3.52×10^{-7}
575	1.22×10^{-6}
629	3.02×10^{-5}
647	8.59×10^{-5}
666	2.19×10^{-4}
683	5.12×10^{-4}
700	1.16×10^{-3}
716	2.50×10^{-3}
781	3.95×10^{-2}

5. The data below were obtained by Bodenstein for the reaction

$$2NO + O_2 \xrightarrow{k} 2NO_2$$

$T (°K)$	k_{obs} [(cm^3)^2 molecules^{-2} sec^{-1}]
270	25.46×10^{-39}
370	12.89×10^{-39}
470	9.04×10^{-39}
570	7.59×10^{-39}
670	6.86×10^{-39}

What can you conclude from these data?

6. Assume that the laws of thermodynamics apply to a transition state molecule, and rewrite Equation (9–7) in terms of the free energy of activation. What quantity in transition state theory corresponds to the preexponential factor in the Arrhenius equation?

7. For many series of related reactions it often happens that the standard free-energy changes parallel the free energies of activation. According to transition state theory, what does this imply regarding the rates and equilibrium constants in a series of related reactions? This parallel activity of $\Delta G°$ and $\Delta G^{\ddagger}$ is the basis of all *linear free-energy relations*.

8. Above $-90°C$, 1, 1-difluorocyclohexane(I) undergoes a dynamic interconversion between two forms of equal ener gy.

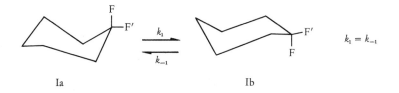

Ia   Ib

$k_1 = k_{-1}$

Gutowsky and coworkers (in 1965) measured the rate of ring inversion in carbon disulfide solution from $+6$ to $-71°$ C.

temp (°C)	k_1 (sec^{-1})	temp (°C)	k_1 (sec^{-1})	temp (°C)	k_1 (sec^{-1})
$+6$	3.36×10^4	-16	2.04×10^4	-38.5	3.65×10^3
$+1$	3.36	-19	1.70	-45	1.89
-3	2.82	-25	1.12	-50	1.19
-5.5	2.94	-29	0.88	-56	0.75
-9	2.65	-31	7.30×10^3	-62	0.38
-9.5	2.54	-35	4.50	-67	0.21
				-71	0.14

(a) What is $\Delta \tilde{G}°$ for the process?

(b) Use the Arrhenius equation and calculate the activation energy for the process.

(c) Calculate $\Delta G^{\ddagger}$ for every temperature below $-9.5°$ C in the table. What does the near constancy of this quantity tell you about $\Delta S^{\ddagger}$?

X

Classification of Reactions, Reactants, and Mechanisms

Before proceeding with further discussion of kinetics and mechanisms, it is useful at this point to introduce some frequently used vocabulary. These terms are words of classification which merely make conversation more convenient. We begin by stating that reactions take place between a *reagent* and a *substrate;* the latter is the species that is acted upon by the former. This division is somewhat arbitrary, and how we decide, in a given case, which is which depends upon our emphasis and point of view.

10–1 TYPES OF REACTIONS

Reactions are best classified according to the form of their stoichiometry. *Substitution* reactions, as the name implies, are reactions of the type where A reacts with B in a displacement fashion to form C and D.

$$CH_3\!-\!H + Cl_2 \xrightarrow{h\nu} CH_3\!-\!Cl + HCl \qquad (10\text{–}1)$$

$$CH_3Cl + Br^- \rightarrow CH_3Br + Cl^- \qquad (10\text{–}2)$$

[85]

The first reaction above is the formation of methyl chloride from methane; a hydrogen has been substituted by a chlorine. In the second reaction a bromide displaces chloride from methyl chloride.

Addition reactions are reactions of the type where A combines with B to give only C; there must be fewer distinct product species than reactant species. This usage of the term "addition reaction" pertains only to the stoichiometry of the process under consideration, and is independent of any mechanistic details.

$$CH_2 = CH_2 + Cl_2 \rightarrow CH_2\text{---}CH_2$$

$$\text{Ethylene} \qquad\qquad\quad | \quad\ | \qquad\qquad (10\text{-}3)$$

$$Cl \quad Cl$$

1,2-Dichloroethane

$$H_2O + SO_3 \rightarrow H_2SO_4 \qquad\qquad (10\text{-}4)$$

Equation (10-3) represents the addition of chlorine to ethylene to give 1,2-dichloroethane. Reaction (10-4) is formally one of the steps in the lead chamber process for production of sulfuric acid.

Elimination reactions are in essence the reverse of addition reactions. There must be fewer distinct reactant species than product species.

$$HSO_5^- \rightarrow HSO_3^- + O_2 \qquad\qquad (10\text{-}5)$$

Peroxo-   Hydrogen
hydrogen   sulfite
sulfate   monoanion
mono-
anion

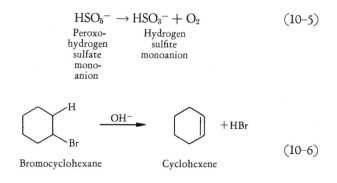

Bromocyclohexane   Cyclohexene

$$(10\text{-}6)$$

Reaction (10-5) is the elimination of molecular oxygen from the monoanion of Caro's acid (peroxosulfuric acid). Reaction (10-6) is the elimination of the elements of HBr from bromocyclohexane by treatment with strong base.

Many reactions are best described as rearrangements, that is, the basic skeleton of the starting system changes to give a skeleton of different structure.

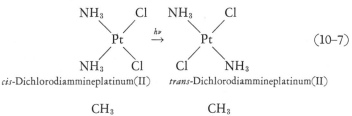

$$\text{(10-7)}$$

cis-Dichlorodiammineplatinum(II)   *trans*-Dichlorodiammineplatinum(II)

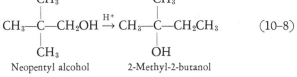

$$\text{(10-8)}$$

Neopentyl alcohol   2-Methyl-2-butanol

In Equation (10-7) the *cis*-dichlorodiammineplatinum(II) rearranges on irradiation with ultraviolet light to the trans isomer, and in Reaction (10-8) neopentyl alcohol undergoes an acid-catalyzed rearrangement to yield, among other products, 2-methyl-2-butanol.

It follows that if we can write an equation for a reaction, then we can classify the reaction. This does not, however, guarantee that the reaction will follow that stoichiometry; indeed, it will not guarantee that the reaction will even occur. The four classes presented above are not mutually exclusive. For example, in the presence of acid as a catalyst, pinacol is transformed into pinacolone.

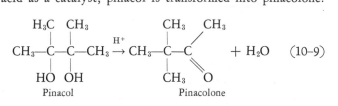

$$\text{(10-9)}$$

Pinacol   Pinacolone

This is clearly an example of a reaction that is both a rearrangement and an elimination.

A large number of important reactions are classified as reduction-oxidation, or *redox*, reactions. In a redox reaction, the oxidation level of the reductant is increased and that of the oxidant is decreased. The criterion for oxidation level is usually the oxidation numbers of the elements in the compounds. Some redox reactions may involve simple transfer of electrons from the reductant to the oxidant; in others the changes may also be described as involving addition and elimination or substitution reactions.

$$\underset{\text{Oxidant}}{Cl_2} \;+\; \underset{\text{Reductant}}{2I^-} \rightarrow I_2 + 2Cl^- \tag{10-10}$$

$$\underset{\text{Oxidant}}{\overset{H}{\underset{H}{\diagup}}\!\!\diagdown C{=}O} + \underset{\text{Reductant}}{H_2} \rightarrow H_3COH \tag{10-11}$$

$$\underset{\text{Oxidant}}{3F_2} \;+\; \underset{\text{Reductant}}{S} \rightarrow SF_6 \tag{10-12}$$

The fact that Reaction (10–12) is clearly an addition reaction classified as either redox or addition is no cause for alarm. The reaction classes are simply defined so broadly that they overlap.

10–2   TYPES OF REACTANTS

Reactant characteristics may also be classified, although not as rigorously as reactions. Here again, the classes are not mutually exclusive and from a totally unbiased point of view a given reactant may be appropriately described by two or more adjectives. Further, some reactants are quite ambivalent and can be classified one way or the other depending on the reaction being considered. In this sense reactant characteristics are relative terms.

A very widespread classification of reactant characteristics is that of *electrophilic* (El) and *nucleophilic* (Nu), which mean literally "electron-seeking" and "nucleus-seeking," respectively. To a zeroth approximation these terms may be likened to the terms acidic and basic. Thus, all Lewis acids are electrophiles and all bases are nucleophiles.

$$F_3B + :NH_3 \rightarrow F_3\bar{B}{-}\overset{+}{N}H_3 \tag{10-13}$$
$$(El + \leftarrow Nu \rightarrow El \leftarrow Nu)$$

We recognize ammonia as a nucleophile, because it has a tendency to involve its lone-pair electrons in a bond to an electron-deficient atom, such as, for example, the boron atom in boron trifluoride. Identity of basicity with nucleophilicity is neither convenient nor accurate; conventional usage reserves nucleophilicity for discussion of rate phenomena, while basicity is employed in talking about equilibria. In the reaction given below chlorine could appropriately be called an electrophile, but one does not ordinarily regard it as an acid.

$$X_3N: + Cl_2 \rightarrow [X_3\overset{+}{N}{-}Cl]Cl^- \qquad (10\text{-}14)$$

A series of nucleophiles may be arranged in the following order of decreasing basicity toward H^+:

$$OH^- > N_3^- > C_6H_5NH_2 > S_2O_3^{2-} > SCN^- > Br^- > I^-$$

However, if the relative nucleophilic reactivities toward a standard substrate such as methyl bromide are measured, this order turns out to be significantly different:

$$S_2O_3^{2-} > I^- > SCN^- > C_6H_5NH_2 > OH^- > N_3^- > Br^-$$

Basicity toward protons is only one manifestation of nucleophilic reactivity.

Two additional ways of classifying reactant characteristics are (a) *nonpolar* versus *polar*, and (b) *oxidant* versus *reductant*. The first set of characteristics is best used for describing reactants which we do not wish to call electrophilic or nucleophilic. Thus, in the chlorination of methane, Equation (10-1), it is not convenient to refer to either methane or chlorine as either an electrophile or a nucleophile; rather, they are nonpolar reactants. Both products are polar species. The second set of characteristics is self-evident and familiar. In the reaction of $FeCl_2$ with chlorine, clearly the chlorine acts as an oxidant and $FeCl_2$ as a reductant.

$$2FeCl_2 + Cl_2 \rightarrow 2FeCl_3 \qquad (10\text{-}15)$$

10-3 TYPES OF MECHANISMS

Reaction mechanisms are more difficult to classify rigorously. One way is to call all mechanisms either *chain* or *nonchain* mechanisms. By the former we mean a mechanism which includes two or more *chain-propagating steps* which recur in a cyclic manner. An ex-

ample will clarify the point.   The mechanism for the chlorination
of methane is outlined below:

$$Cl_2 \xrightarrow{h\nu} 2Cl\cdot \qquad \text{Chain initiation} \quad (10\text{--}16)$$

$$CH_4 + Cl\cdot \rightarrow CH_3\cdot + HCl \;\big\} \qquad\qquad\qquad (10\text{--}17)$$

$$\qquad\qquad\qquad\qquad \text{Chain propagation}$$

$$CH_3\cdot + Cl_2 \rightarrow CH_3Cl + Cl\cdot \big\} \qquad\qquad (10\text{--}18)$$

$$2Cl\cdot \rightarrow Cl_2 \qquad\qquad\qquad\qquad (10\text{--}19)$$

$$CH_3\cdot + Cl\cdot \rightarrow CH_3Cl \qquad \text{Chain termination} (10\text{--}20)$$

$$CH_3\cdot + CH_3\cdot \rightarrow CH_3CH_3 \qquad\qquad\qquad (10\text{--}21)$$

Chlorine atoms which are produced in the chain-initiation step
[Equation (10–16)] react with methane in a chain-propagation step
[Equation (10–17)].   The result of Equation (10–18) is to produce
new chlorine atoms which can react with new methane molecules
over several cycles.   Reaction is ultimately brought to a standstill
by means of the chain-termination steps [Equations (10–19) to
(10–21)].

Nonchain mechanisms have been most extensively studied.   Their
complete description includes classification of the overall reaction
stoichiometry, classification of a reactant characteristic, and quite
often, the mode of activation in the rate-determining step.

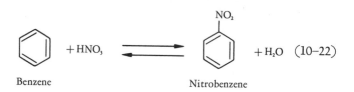

Benzene   Nitrobenzene

Equation (10–22) represents the nitration of benzene; overall, this is
a substitution reaction.   The rate-determining step for the plausible
mechanism is

where the important attacking reagent is NO_2^+ which is an electrophile. Since two species are bonded together in the rate-determining step, we shall refer to the mechanism as an *associative* mechanism. Our mechanism for nitration can then be described rather completely as an associative, electrophilic substitution. A common way of abbreviating this description is by means of the symbolism S_E2. In this expression, S stands for substitution, E stands for electrophilic, and the 2 signifies a bimolecular, associative-type mechanism.

For the overall reaction

$$[Co(CN)_5(OH_2)]^{2-} + I^- \rightleftharpoons [Co(CN)_5 I]^{3-} + H_2O \quad (10\text{--}24)$$

a plausible mechanism involves the rate-determining step

$$[Co(CN)_5(OH_2)]^{2-} \rightarrow [Co(CN)_5]^{2-} + H_2O \quad (10\text{--}25)$$

Since iodide is a nucleophile and since in Equation (10–25) the activation energy in the rate-determining step must come primarily through breaking of the bond between cobalt and water, this mechanism is described as a *dissociative* nucleophilic substitution, or S_N1 for short.

Examples of associative, nucleophilic substitution reactions are plentiful. Equations (10–26) and (10–27) show two specific cases which have been well documented.

$$Pt(NH_3)_3Cl^+ + I^- \rightarrow Pt(NH_3)_3I^+ + Cl^- \quad (10\text{--}26)$$
$$CH_3Br + I^- \rightarrow CH_3I + Br^- \quad (10\text{--}27)$$

As would be anticipated, the mechanisms of these reactions may be referred to using the shorthand S_N2.

10–4 SUMMARY

At this point we have considered the study of elementary reactions, an example of the investigation of a reaction mechanism, and generalized theories of reaction rates. There remains the all-important problem of using these concepts to understand reactivity relationships shown in the reactions of several million known compounds. Obviously, we cannot attempt to cover such a broad field comprehensively in a small introductory text. In the following chapters we will concentrate mainly on a single type of reaction, nucleophilic substitution, and see how mechanisms and reactivity vary in this one type of reaction as we tour the periodic table. Other reactions, such as redox reactions, could have been chosen and used to show coherent patterns of behavior. However, the choice of nucleophilic substitution is especially logical, since well over half of all known reactions can be placed in this class.

EXERCISES

1. Classify the following reactions as far as possible:

(a) $BF_3 + NH_3 \rightarrow H_3\overset{+}{N}-\overset{-}{B}F_3$

(b) $NH_4CNO \overset{\Delta}{\rightarrow} NH_2-\overset{\overset{\displaystyle O}{\displaystyle \|}}{C}-NH_2$

(c) $CHCl_3 + OH^- \rightarrow H_2O + :CCl_2 + Cl^-$

(d)

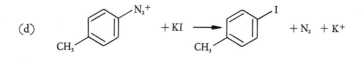

$+ KI \longrightarrow$ $+ N_2 + K^+$

(e) $Sn^{4+} + 2Fe^{2+} \rightleftharpoons Sn^{2+} + 2Fe^{3+}$

(f)

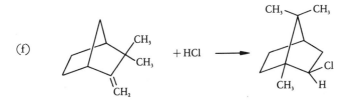

$+ HCl \longrightarrow$

(g) $trans$-$[Co(NH_3)_4(OH)(Cl)]^+ \overset{Slow}{\underset{-Cl^-}{\longrightarrow}} [Co(NH_3)_4(OH)]^{2+}$

$\overset{H_2O}{\longrightarrow} trans$-$[Co(NH_3)_4(OH)(H_2O)]^{2+}$

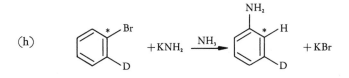

(h)

2. Which of the following reagents could properly be described as polar: CCl_4, NH_3, *trans*-$Pt(NH_3)_2Cl_2$, benzene, H_2O_2, hydrazine, $CH_3—CH_3$, CS_2?

3. A common reaction of the species dichlorocarbene (I) is addition to an olefinic double bond:

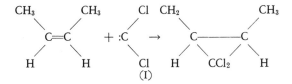

Is CCl_2 acting as an electrophile or as a nucleophile?

4. Which of the following species are likely to behave as Lewis acids and which as Lewis bases?

HCCl₃ $(C_6H_5)_3C^+$

                      SbF_5

                                         H_2O

FeCl₃ $(CH_3CH_2)_3C—O^-$

B(OCH₃)₃   SO₃

HS⁻   Br⁺

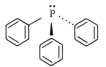

5. The equilibrium constant for the dissociation of the acid $HS_2O_3^-$ is more than a trillion times larger than that for H_2O, yet OH^- reacts with the substrate methyl bromide about 150 times slower than does $S_2O_3^{2-}$. What can you conclude from this example?

XI

Reaction Chemistry of Compounds of the Second-Row Elements with Emphasis on Boron

With the brief introduction to kinetics and mechanics that has been presented so far, we are now ready to return to the examination of some interesting chemical reactions. Attention will be directed toward compounds of the second-row elements with the intention of trying to correlate and make sense out of the large body of information on the chemistry of these compounds. To do this one must compare and contrast the known chemistry of related compounds and hopefully interpret the results in terms of electronic structural models and other aspects of molecular structure.

11-1 AN OUTLINE OF REACTIONS OF COMPOUNDS OF SECOND-ROW ELEMENTS

We begin by noting that salts of the first two members of the second row are essentially ionic solids with high melting points, high solubilities in water, and otherwise unspectacular chemistry. Lithium fluoride and lithium carbonate are typical examples. Beryllium is less electropositive in all its chemical behavior than lithium, so that its compounds have significantly more covalent bonding. No more will be said about lithium and beryllium until Chapter 14. The following sketch gives a sprinkling of the chemistry associated with compounds of the remaining second-row elements. There are obvious similarities and differences in the results for ostensibly related compounds, and it is just these similarities and differences which need to be rationalized and will thus form the central theme of the next few chapters.

BF_3 Boron trifluoride reacts rapidly with water to form variously hydrated boric acids and also tetrafluoroborate anion (BF_4^-). This latter species will react more slowly with water to give boric acids also. With 50% aqueous HF, boric acid is converted to HBF_4. Obviously, in these examples we have rapid substitution reactions in which fluorines or oxygen becomes bound to boron.

BCl_3 Boron trichloride, however, reacts rapidly with water in an essentially irreversible process to give boric acids plus chloride ion. No BCl_4^- is detectable.

CF_4 In contrast to boron halides, this material is very inert. No reaction with water or other more powerful nucleophiles is known; carbon tetrafluoride can be made to react with very electropositive metals.

CH_3F Replacement of three fluorines by hydrogens in CF_4 gives methyl fluoride. This will react very slowly in concentrated aqueous acid to give methanol.

CH_3Cl Methyl chloride is much more reactive than the fluoride toward nucleophiles. Dilute aqueous base reacts with CH_3Cl also to give methanol.

NF_3 Nitrogen trifluoride is inert toward water; it is, however, a good oxidizing agent. It will also react slowly with boiling aqueous acid.

NF_2H Replacement of one of the fluorines in NF_3 by hydrogen produces this most remarkable substance, difluoramine. It reacts very rapidly with almost any nucleophile. Obviously, in this case one has mechanisms operating which are not possible or likely in the case of NF_3. Large changes in reactivity as a result of only modest changes in structure are often the signal for operation of different mechanisms.

NCl₃   In contrast to NF_3, the chlorinated material (which is very explosive) reacts rapidly with water. Ammonia and hypochlorous acid are the products of this reaction instead of the anticipated nitrous acid and chloride ions. The observed products are therefore quite likely *kinetically-controlled products*.

NH₃   The chemistry of this nucleophile is well known and need not be elaborated upon.

OF₂   Oxygen difluoride reacts readily with strong aqueous base to form elemental oxygen and fluoride ions. With water it reacts much more slowly, although it explodes with steam.

OCl₂   The analogous dichloride is not inert to water; in fact, there is rapid establishment of the following equilibrium: $H_2O + OCl_2 \rightleftharpoons 2HOCl$.

F₂   Elemental fluorine reacts with aqueous base to give OF_2, and reacts only slowly with water.

11-2 MECHANISMS FOR BORON CHEMISTRY

The above outline represents a very wide spectrum of reactivities. We can begin our discussion with the case of boron trifluoride in which, it is recalled, the boron is electron-deficient. The three fluorine atoms contribute a small amount of π bonding, and this is taken into account in the molecular orbital picture of BF_3, but for the most part we should expect BF_3 to react with electron-donors. With water (in analogy to the case with ammonia) one might expect

$$BF_3 + H_2O \rightleftharpoons F_3\bar{B}-\overset{+}{O}H_2$$

The expected "hydrate" has a melting point of 10.18°C, and spectroscopic studies indicate that it is not ionized in the solid state. A "dihydrate" which may have the structure $[H_3O^+][F_3\bar{B}OH]$ has a melting point of 6.36°C. This structure has not been determined, however. Presumably, it should be possible to carry out substitution reactions on the "tetrahedral" boron in this system. Eventually, we would like to have $[H_3O^+][F_3\bar{B}OH]$ converted into $(HO)_3B$, which is a boric acid, one of the observed products. A possible mechanism might be the following:

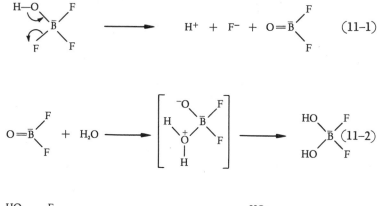

$$H^+ + F^- + O=\bar{B}\begin{matrix} F \\ \\ F \end{matrix} \qquad (11\text{-}1)$$

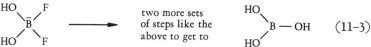

$$(11\text{-}2)$$

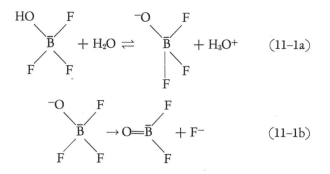

There are details about this mechanism over which we ought to worry. For example, perhaps it is better to let $HO\bar{B}F_3$ come to equilibrium with its conjugate base which then loses fluoride ion to give the hypothesized $O\bar{B}F_2$,

$$(11\text{-}1a)$$

$$(11\text{-}1b)$$

Naturally, kinetics will not tell us if this is so unless Equation (11–1a) represents the slow step of the reaction.

We might also wonder if departure of the fluoride ion in Equation (11–1) is assisted in the rate-determining step by water so that general acid catalysis should actually be observed.[1] Our observed rate law in this case is expected to have the form

$$\text{Rate} = k_1[\text{HOBF}_3][\text{H}_2\text{O}] + k_2[\text{HOBF}_3][\text{H}_3\text{O}^+]$$
$$+ k_3[\text{HOBF}_3][\text{HF}] + \text{Others}$$

Here is a case where kinetics might be of great help in deciding on the merits of a particular mechanism. Unfortunately, there are no available data on this reaction to guide us. The other observed product of the reaction of BF_3 with water could arise simply by

$$\text{F}^- + \text{BF}_3 \rightleftharpoons \text{BF}_4^- \qquad (11\text{–}4)$$

Structurally, $HOBF_3^-$ and BF_4^- are similar, yet the former apparently hydrolyzes very rapidly whereas the latter does so only slowly. A rationalization of this difference probably lies not in the difference between the B—F and B—O bond strengths, but rather in the fact that $HOBF_3^-$ contains a removable proton which is available for participation in the reaction. In fact, it is this consideration which led to the proposed mechanism given above.

We could now ask how BF_4^- hydrolyzes at all. Several possible mechanisms come to mind. We could have water and BF_4^- (in an associative process) form an intermediate adduct which then loses fluoride ion to give a species which is formally identical with the adduct of water and BF_3:

$$\text{H}_2\text{O} + \text{BF}_4^- \rightarrow [\text{H}_2\text{O}^+\!\!-\!\!\text{BF}_4^{2-}] \rightarrow \text{H}_2\text{O}^+\!\!-\!\!\overline{\text{B}}\text{F}_3 + \text{F}^- \quad (11\text{–}5)$$
$$\downarrow$$
$$\text{etc.}$$

We are inclined to discard this mechanism because it requires boron in the initial adduct to accommodate five groups with a total of ten electrons for σ bonding. Second-row elements, with only $2s$ and $2p$ valence orbitals, are not prepared for a coordination number of five.

---

[1] General acid catalysis refers to catalysis of a reaction by means of any Lewis acid as opposed to specific acid catalysis which is limited to catalysis by the hydronium ion only.

Another possible mechanism is a concerted attack of water and elimination of F^- via a transition state that might have the shape of a trigonal bipyramid.

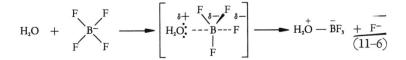

$$(11\text{-}6)$$

This is not quite the same as the mechanism suggested in Reaction (10-5) because a transition state is not expected to be a stable molecule.

Finally, a third and very plausible mechanism can be written. It is likely that in solution BF_4^- is slowly equilibrated with BF_3 and F^-. Hydrolysis then occurs by reaction of the small equilibrium amount of BF_3 with water.

$$BF_4^- \underset{\text{Slow}}{\overset{k}{\rightleftharpoons}} BF_3 + F^-$$

$$H_2O \qquad (k < 1) \qquad (11\text{-}7)$$

$$HOBF_3^- + H^+$$

This is a *dissociative* mechanism. At the present time no good choice can be made between mechanisms (11-6) and (11-7).

Boron trichloride is different from the trifluoride in that its hydrolysis produces no BCl_4^- ions. It is necessary to ask wherein lies the difference. One important factor may be the relatively larger size of chlorine versus fluorine so that BCl_4^- is somewhat more sterically congested than BF_4^-. Another consideration probably lies in the difference between the B—F and B—Cl bond energies. Reliable data are scarce for boron compounds. Bond energy values[2] for

---

[2] The bond energy value BE_n for a bond in a molecule of k bonds is that energy such that the sum

$$\sum_{n=1}^{k} BE_n$$

equals the heat of atomization of the compound.

the B—F and B—Cl bonds are approximately 139 and 94 kcal mole^{-1}, respectively. This great difference implies that K_1 is greater than K_2 in the following equations:

$$F^- + BF_3 \rightleftharpoons BF_4^- \quad K_1 \tag{11-8}$$

$$Cl^- + BCl_3 \rightleftharpoons BCl_4^- \quad K_2 \tag{11-9}$$

Since both the steric factor and the difference in bond energies work in the same direction, it will probably not be possible to separate them. Furthermore, it is not easy to predict whether BCl_4^- should hydrolyze faster or slower than BF_4^-; however, we will be able to make some shrewd guesses as to the probable relative reactivities after considering the reactivities in nucleophilic substitution reactions of compounds containing C—F and C—Cl bonds.

EXERCISES

1. Values of the ionization potential and electron affinity of the second-row elements are given in the table below.

	Li	*Be*	*B*	*C*	*N*	*0*	*F*	*Ne*
IP (eV)	5.39	9.52	8.30	11.26	14.54	13.61	17.42	21.56
EA (eV)	0.54	−0.6	0.2	1.25	−0.1	1.47	3.45	—

Discuss how these data may be expected to be reflected in the chemisty of the second-row elements.

2. The simplest boron hydride, BH_3, has never been isolated. Its dimer, diborane, does exist as a stable molecule, however, and has the following interesting structure:

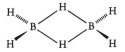

The bonds to the two bridging hydrogens are not conventional two-electron B—H bonds. We may conveniently refer to them as "bridging" bonds.

Assuming the bond energy of a normal B—H bond to be 93.0 kcal mole^{-1}, and taking the sublimation energy of boron to be 140.9 kcal mole^{-1}, calculate the standard heat of formation of BH_3. If the standard heat of formation of diborane is taken to be 7.6 kcal mole^{-1}, estimate the strength of one of the bridging B—H bonds in the material.

4. Predict what will happen when the following processes are carried out:
(a) Methyl borate, $B(OCH_3)_3$, is added to an aqueous sodium hydroxide solution.
(b) Diborane is burned in an excess of dry air.
(c) Boron trifluoride is passed into absolute methanol, CH_3OH.
(d) Diborane is bubbled into water.

5. In much of its chemistry diborane behaves as if it were the half-species BH_3. Thus, diborane reacts with olefins to form trialkylboranes

$$B_2H_6 + 6RCH{=}CH_2 \rightarrow 2(RCH_2CH_2)_3B$$

This is a synthetically useful result, since the resulting trialkylboranes are easily cleaved by acids such as acetic acid to give saturated hydrocarbons and borate esters

$$3CH_3COOH + BR_3 \rightarrow 3R{-}H + B(OCOCH_3)_3$$

Formulate a reasonable mechanism for this last step.

6. The standard enthalpies of reaction of trimethylamine with diborane and boron trifluoride are given below.

$$2(CH_3)_3N(g) + B_2H_6(g) \rightarrow 2(CH_3)_3N{-}BH_3(g) \qquad \Delta\tilde{H}^\circ = -3.46 \text{ kcal mole}^{-1}$$
$$(CH_3)_3N(g) + BF_3(g) \rightarrow (CH_3)_3N{-}BF_3(g) \qquad \Delta\tilde{H}^\circ = -26.6 \text{ kcal mole}^{-1}$$

What do these data suggest about the relative acidities of BH_3 and BF_3 (toward trimethylamine)? How would you rank these two substances in comparison with trimethylborane?

XII

Reaction Chemistry of Compounds of Carbon, Nitrogen, Oxygen, and Fluorine

12-1 MECHANISMS FOR CARBON

As mentioned in the previous chapter, carbon tetrafluoride is inert to most nucleophiles. Using suitable values for free energies of formation we predict that the equilibrium for the following reaction should lie far to the right:

$$CF_4 + 2H_2O \rightleftharpoons CO_2 + 4HF \qquad (12\text{--}1)$$

Consequently, we know that reaction fails to take place because there is no pathway that allows a significantly rapid *rate* of reaction. We recall that in the case of fully fluorinated boron (BF_4^-) hydrolysis is not rapid although it does occur to a measurable extent. In considering possible mechanisms that might have operated for a hypothetical hydrolysis, we included a dissociative mechanism that *might* be applicable to the carbon compound.

$$CF_4 \rightleftharpoons CF_3^+ + F^-$$

$$\downarrow H_2O$$

$$\overset{+}{H_2O}\!\!-\!\!CF_3 \xrightarrow{\ -HF\ } HO\!\!-\!\!\overset{+}{C}F_2 \rightarrow And\ so\ on \qquad (12\text{--}2)$$

The trifluoromethyl cation can be expected to be a very unstable species because of the fact that three very electronegative atoms are attached to an atom that is already electron-deficient. Clearly the instability of CF_3^+ could be a good rationalization for the absence of the above kind of mechanism for hydrolysis of CF_4. We also considered a concerted mechanism for hydrolysis of BF_4^- and should also consider such a path for reaction of the carbon compound. Because the central-atom formal charge is now formally 0 rather than -1 as in the case of BF_4^-, carbon tetrafluoride might be expected to react with nucleophiles more rapidly than tetrafluoroborate.

$$HO^- + CF_4 \xrightarrow{k_1} \left[HO\text{-----}\underset{\underset{F}{|}}{\overset{\overset{F\diagdown\ \diagup F}{}}{C}}\text{-----}F \right]^- \rightarrow HOCF_3 + F^- \qquad (12\text{--}3)$$

$$HO^- + BF_4^- \xrightarrow{k_2} \left[HO\text{-----}\underset{\underset{F}{|}}{\overset{\overset{F\diagdown\ \diagup F}{}}{B}}\text{-----}F \right]^{2-} \rightarrow HO\bar{B}F_4 + F^- \qquad (12\text{--}4)$$

Prediction: $k_2 \ll k_1$

Since CF_4 is actually very inert toward aqueous base, we conclude that Reaction (12–3) is immeasurably slow. If we believe the above inference, we also draw the conclusion that hydrolysis of BF_4^- cannot involve a mechanism such as Reaction (12–4). This is perhaps the strongest argument in favor of the dissociative mechanism for reaction of BF_4^- with water.

Note the logical sequence used in assigning mechanism:

(1) The dissociative mechanism is predicted to be faster with BF_4^- than CF_4.

(2) The concerted mechanism is predicted to be faster with CF_4 than with BF_4^-.

(3) Since BF_4^- reacts with water and CF_4 does not, the dissociative mechanism must be assigned to the reaction of BF_4^-.

(4) We can formulate no judgment as to which path would be easier with CF_4, since measurable reaction does not occur by either mechanism.

Methyl chloride reacts readily with strongly basic nucleophiles (such as OH^-) although reaction with neutral water solution is very slow. Very extensive study of the kinetics of the reaction, as well as of reactions of other alkyl chlorides, has provided convincing evidence that the substitution reaction proceeds via a concerted, associative mechanism. The transition state is assumed to have the configuration of a trigonal bipyramid.

$$HO^- + CH_3Cl \rightarrow \left[\begin{array}{c} H \quad H \\ \diagdown \diagup \\ HO\text{-----}C\text{-----}Cl \\ | \\ H \end{array} \right]^- \rightarrow CH_3OH + Cl^- \qquad (12\text{--}5)$$

Methyl fluoride is enormously less reactive than the chloride, despite the fact that data for free energies of formation indicate that equilibrium in Reaction (12–6) should lie far to the right.

$$H_2O + CH_3F \rightleftharpoons CH_3OH + HF \qquad (12\text{--}6)$$

Why then, is CH_3F so inert? A possible factor is the difference between the C—F (94 kcal mole^{-1}) and C—Cl (73 kcal mole^{-1}) bond strengths. We do not know whether the high bond energies of the products, and the large solvation energy of fluoride ion, will start to "pay us back" in time to allow the transition state to have a reasonably low energy. In order to learn more, we can consider related exchange reactions in which overall thermodynamics is not a factor. For example, the following reactions can be carried out using tracer-labeled nucleophiles so that the bonds made and broken are essentially identical:[1]

$$*Cl^- + CH_3Cl \xrightarrow{k_1} CH_3*Cl + Cl^- \qquad (12\text{-}7)$$

$$*Br^- + CH_3Br \xrightarrow{k_2} CH_3*Br + Br^- \qquad (12\text{-}8)$$

Experimentally, it is found that $k_2 > k_1$, a difference which *must* be attributed to kinetic factors, and we now ask the reason.

At least part of the answer lies in the fact that the valence orbitals of chlorine are larger than those of fluorine so that the interaction of outer electrons with the nucleus is smaller. In the vicinity of a point charge we should get a bigger response from chlorine than from fluorine. Expressed another way we mean that chlorine is more *polarizable* (deformable) than fluorine and hence will adapt more readily to any stress, such as bond stretching, to form a transition state. In any event the heavier halide ions are regularly better (faster) leaving groups in nucleophilic substitution reactions with second-row elements as the central atoms.

If a hydrogen of CH_3F were to be replaced by a hydroxyl group, the substance fluoromethanol would be obtained. By analogy with $HOBF_3^-$ we should expect fluoromethanol to hydrolyze very rapidly by an elimination-addition sequence.

$$\underset{\text{Formaldehyde}}{HOCH_2F \rightarrow H_2C{=}O} + HF \qquad (12\text{-}9)$$

$$\underset{\text{Methanediol}}{H_2CO + H_2O \rightarrow HOCH_2OH} \qquad (12\text{-}10)$$

All attempts to prepare $HOCH_2F$ invariably lead to formaldehyde. The latter is stable in the gas phase but in water solution it exists virtually exclusively as methanediol $[CH_2(OH)_2]$.

12-2   MECHANISMS FOR NITROGEN

It comes as no surprise that NF_3 reacts only very slowly with nucleophiles. This is simply what an extrapolation from BF_4^- and

---

[1] The general reaction of $X^- + RY \rightleftharpoons RX + Y^-$ where X^- and Y^- are halides is called the Finkelstein reaction.

CF_4 would predict since all three compounds have filled valence shells and have fluoride as the only potential leaving group. Nitrogen trifluoride does hydrolyze slowly in strong acid, forming nitrous acid and hydrogen fluoride. Acid catalysis indicates that departure of fluoride needs assistance. These facts do not distinguish between dissociative and concerted mechanisms for reaction of NF_3. However, examination of the details leads to the prediction that reaction by the dissociative mechanism should be faster with CF_4 than with NF_3 since a cationic intermediate derived from the nitrogen compound should be the less stable.

$$F_3C-F \ \cdots \ H_3O^+ \xrightarrow{k_1} F_3C^+ + HF + H_2O \qquad (12\text{--}11)$$

$$F_2N-F \ \cdots \ H_3O^+ \xrightarrow{k_2} F_2N^+ + HF + H_2O \qquad (12\text{--}12)$$
$$\text{Prediction: } k_1 > k_2$$

Since NF_3 is actually more reactive than CF_4, we prefer to assign a concerted mechanism:

$$H - \overset{\cdot\cdot}{O}: \ + \ F_2N-F \ \text{----} \ H_3O^+ \longrightarrow H_2\overset{+}{O}NF_2 \ + \ HF \ + \ H_2O$$
$$\underset{H}{|}$$
$$(12\text{--}13)$$

The higher reactivity of NF_3 is surely partly due to a large difference in bond energies ($N-F = 65$ kcal mole^{-1}, $C-F = 102$ kcal mole^{-1}) although there may also be an important contribution because the nitrogen center in NF_3 is more accessible to the water than in the four-coordinate cases. We call this a favorable *steric effect*.

Question: From what has been said above, we would predict that the following reaction would have a large rate constant:

$$HO^- \ + \ F_2N-F \ \text{----} \ H_3O^+ \longrightarrow HONF_2 \ + \ HF \ + \ H_2O \qquad (12\text{--}14)$$

The prediction is hard to test. Why? Why is $HONF_2$ an unknown compound?

Nitrogen trichloride reacts rapidly with water. This may be partially due to the fact that the N—Cl bond energy (46 kcal mole^{-1}) is less than that of the N—F bond. However, the products are ammonia and hypochlorous acid, rather than nitrous acid and hydrochloric acid. This indicates that the nucleophile attacks chlorine rather than nitrogen!

$$H_2\ddot{O}: + \quad Cl—NCl_2 \longrightarrow H_2\overset{+}{O}Cl + NCl_2^{-} \qquad (12\text{--}15)$$

Probably the dichloroamide ion is not produced free since departure of the leaving group is undoubtedly assisted by electrophilic catalysis by water.

$$H_2\ddot{O}: + Cl—\underset{\underset{Cl}{|}}{\overset{\overset{Cl}{|}}{N}}\cdots\cdots H_2O \rightarrow H_2\overset{+}{O}Cl + Cl_2NH + HO^{-} \qquad (12\text{--}16)$$

If this is true the reaction is probably acid-catalyzed, but this has not, to our knowledge, been established. The experiment would be difficult because study of catalysis of a reaction that is very fast anyway is no trivial experimental challenge.

We can ask why carbon tetrachloride does not hydrolyze by attack on chlorine:

$$H_2O + CCl_4 \overset{\text{Why?}}{\not\longrightarrow} HCCl_3 + HOCl \qquad (12\text{--}17)$$

Two reasons are fairly evident. First, Cl_3C^- would be a much poorer leaving group than Cl_2N^-. Second, the unshared pair of electrons of nitrogen in NCl_3 offers a "handle" for the electrophilic interaction with solvent molecules.

Difluoramine (HNF_2) is extremely reactive toward almost any nucleophile. The contrast to NF_3 is so striking as to almost demand that a new mechanism be developed to account for the high reactivity. When this occurs, the usual approach is to try to formulate the "new" mechanism in such a way as to involve "new" structural features directly. In this case an obvious candidate is the presence of an N—H bond in difluoramine. Furthermore, the present case is also keyed by the fact that products formed in reactions of difluoramine are often very different from those expected from simple nucleophilic substitution reactions. The following is an example:

$$CH_3—NH_2 + HNF_2 \rightarrow CH_4 + N_2 + HF \qquad (12\text{-}18)$$

Methylamine   Methane

The H—N bond energy is high ($\sim$95 kcal mole^{-1}), so it is not likely that the reactions involve cleavage to free radicals although such a reaction *might* be the initiating step in an efficient chain reaction. Since nucleophiles are required, it is probable that the reaction involves an acid-base reaction.[2]

$$CH_3NH_2 + HNF_2 \rightleftharpoons CH_3\overset{+}{N}H_3 + :\overset{..}{N}F_2{}^- \qquad (12\text{-}19)$$

Methyl-   Difluoro-
ammonium   amide
ion   ion

We suddenly make progress if we assume that the difluoroamide ion can fall apart to produce fluoronitrene

$$NF_2{}^- \rightarrow :\overset{..}{N}F + F^- \qquad (12\text{-}20)$$

Fluoronitrene

Reaction (12-20) is not intended to appear ordinary; it is extraordinary, but there are other examples. The species NF is highly reactive and its reactivity is predictable on structural grounds. The nitrogen possesses only six valence electrons so it should be a powerful Lewis acid. When generated in water it will react with water but in nonnucleophilic solvents it seeks out a nucleophile. Reaction with methylamine should occur as follows:

$$CH_3—\overset{..}{N}H_2 + :\overset{..}{N}F \rightarrow CH_3—\overset{\displaystyle H}{\underset{\displaystyle H}{\overset{|}{\underset{|}{N^+}}}}—\overset{..}{\underset{..}{N}}F \qquad (12\text{-}21)$$

---

[2] This is pure speculation. If it should turn out that this guess does not lead to a plausible mechanism, we would back off and try something else. The acid-base reaction might turn out to be just a side excursion of the system, rather than a path to products.

The dipolar intermediate should find rapid reactions to stabilize itself further. The following process is one which might come to mind:

$$H_3C - \overset{\overset{\displaystyle H}{|}}{\underset{\underset{\displaystyle H}{|}}{N^+}} - \overset{..}{\underset{..}{N}}F \longrightarrow H_3C - H \;+\; HN{=}NF \qquad (12\text{-}22)$$

The mechanism is not inconceivable, but it involves two kinds of changes that are usually found to be slow: (1) substitution at a saturated, filled shell atom; and (2) making and breaking bonds to carbon. Another kind of change can be visualized that only involves transferring a proton from one electronegative atom to another:

$$CH_3 - \overset{\overset{\displaystyle H}{|}}{\underset{\underset{\displaystyle H}{|}}{N^+}} - \overset{..}{\underset{..}{N}} - F \rightarrow CH_3 - \overset{..}{\underset{\underset{\displaystyle H}{|}}{N}} - \overset{..}{\underset{\underset{\displaystyle H}{|}}{N}} - F \qquad (12\text{-}23)$$

1-Methyl-2-fluorohydrazine

The methylfluorohydrazine is now set up to undergo a fast elimination reaction, similar to those evoked to explain the instability of $HO\overline{B}F_3$ and $HOCH_2F$.

$$CH_3NHNHF \rightarrow CH_3N{=}NH + HF \qquad (12\text{-}24)$$

Methyldiimide

Methyldiimide is not a known compound, so if it is formed, there is probably some rapid path for its destruction, although we do not wish to convey the impression that unknown compounds are necessarily unstable. We might try the following sequence:

$$CH_3N{=}N{-}H \rightarrow CH_3N_2^- + H^+ \qquad (12\text{-}25)$$

$$CH_3{-}N{=}N^- \rightarrow H_3C{:}^- + N_2 \qquad (12\text{-}26)$$

Reaction (12-26) produces a very unstable species, the methyl anion. It may be that the free anion is not formed because some proton donor is involved in bonding to carbon during the fragmentation step. However, this is not necessarily required. Reaction (12–26) will be driven by the fact that a very stable molecule, nitrogen, is formed; the $N{\equiv}N$ bond energy is 225 kcal mole^{-1}, whereas the $N{=}N$ bond is worth only about 100 kcal mole^{-1}.

If the mechanism for reaction of difluoramine with nucleophiles were the only one of its kind, we would probably dismiss it as highly imaginative nonsense. However, there are a number of related examples that have been found where this should occur. Consider the reactivity of the following series of compounds toward aqueous base:

CCl_4	Inert
$CHCl_3$	Quite reactive
CH_2Cl_2	Sluggish
CH_3Cl	Very reactive

Chloroform seems to be out of position in this series, strongly suggesting a unique mechanism. The following is the one that has been well established:

$$CHCl_3 + OH^- \rightarrow :CCl_3^- + H_2O$$

$$\downarrow -Cl^- \qquad\qquad (12\text{–}27)$$

$$:CCl_2 \xrightarrow[\text{Many steps}]{OH^-,\ H_2O} CO \text{ and } HCO_3^-$$

12–3 MECHANISMS FOR OXYGEN AND FLUORINE

Oxygen difluoride falls in the same series as BF_4^-, CF_4, and NF_3. Accordingly, we find in agreement with expectations that it does not undergo nucleophilic attack by water. With aqueous base it reacts as follows:

$$OF_2 + OH^- \rightarrow O_2 + H_2O + F^- \qquad (12\text{–}28)$$

A plausible mechanism, which must necessarily include a means of accounting for formation of an oxygen-oxygen bond begins with a concerted attack on the oxygen with displacement of fluoride ion.

$$HO^- + O\underset{F}{\overset{F}{\big\langle}} \rightarrow HO-OF + F^- \qquad (12\text{-}29)$$

The species HO—OF might conceivably eliminate HF directly to give molecular oxygen. Alternatively, elimination may begin by ionization as an acid to give O_2F^- (recall that hydrogen peroxide is a stronger acid than water). At any rate, analogy to other unknown molecules ($HO\overline{B}F_3$, $HOCH_2F$, CH_3NHNHF) suggests that elimination should occur very rapidly.

$$
\begin{array}{l}
HO-OF \xrightarrow{\;\;-HF\;\;} O_2 \\[4pt]
\Big\downarrow \qquad\qquad \nearrow\;{-F^-} \qquad\qquad (12\text{-}30) \\[4pt]
H^+ + O_2F^-
\end{array}
$$

In either case the reaction is surely driven by the high bond energy of O_2 (118 kcal mole^{-1}), as compared with the O—O single bond energy of about 35–40 kcal mole^{-1}.

In contrast to oxygen difluoride, the dichloride establishes a very fast equilibrium in water to give solutions of hypochlorous acid as well as other species which are always involved in equilibria with HOCl in water.

$$OCl_2 + H_2O \rightleftharpoons 2HOCl \qquad (12\text{-}31)$$

$$3OCl^- \rightleftharpoons 2Cl^- + ClO_3^- \qquad (12\text{-}32)$$

Cleavage probably occurs by nucleophilic attack of water on chlorine as in the case of the hydrolysis of NCl_3.

Finally, in basic solution fluorine reacts to form OF_2. It is not known by what path this occurs, but again, a plausible mechanism that could be drawn consists of a simple nucleophilic displacement of fluoride ion followed by dissociation and an additional displacement reaction.

$$HO^- + F_2 \rightarrow [HO\text{—}F] + F^-$$
$$\searrow$$
$$H^+ + OF^-$$ (12-33)

$$OF^- + F_2 \rightarrow \underset{F}{\overset{F}{\diagdown}} O + F^-$$ (12-34)

The species HOF, which is hypofluorous acid, is an unknown compound. The fact that OF^-, an unknown species, does not accumulate in solution suggests that it is a very reactive nucleophile toward molecular fluorine, probably more reactive than hydroxide ion. This is a surprising inference since OF^- would be expected to be a much weaker base (toward H^+) than OH^-. Several other examples of high nucleophilic reactivity of hypohalite ions are known.

EXERCISES

1. Estimate the equilibrium constant for the reaction described in Equation (12-1); refer either to tables of standard free energies of formation, or else use known values for bond energies and assume a negligible standard entropy change.

2. Consider the following alkyl chloride in which R_1, R_2, and R_3 are different groups:

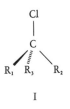

I

Assume that this compound undergoes an associative substitution reaction with OH^- to give the corresponding alcohol. Will the alcohol have the structure II or III on the next page?

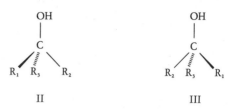

II   III

Is there any difference between these two structures? Compound III is said to have a configuration which is inverted from that of either I or II. Additional information on this phenomenon may be found by consulting any book which discusses optical activity and optical isomerism (for example, see J. D. Roberts and M. C. Caserio, *Basic Principles of Organic Chemistry*, Chapter 17, W. A. Benjamin, Inc., New York, 1965).

Whether compound I will react with nucleophiles by a dissociative or an associative mechanism is dependent on the nature of the R groups. Suppose that another representative of I is treated with OH⁻. This time a dissociative mechanism prevails and we are able to isolate equal amounts of both II and III. What does this suggest about the structure of the intermediate ion in this reaction?

3. In order to convert alcohols into chlorides, we often treat the former with the reagent thionyl chloride,

Suppose we treat compound II of Exercise 2 with this reagent in some suitable solvent. Try your hand at formulating a mechanism for the reaction which is consistent with the following facts:

(a) The chloride isolated mainly shows retention of configuration, that is, it is mainly I.

(b) We can isolate an intermediate in the reaction which contains sulfur and chloride.

(c) Decay of this intermediate is first order.

4. Hydrazine is commonly prepared by treatment of a large excess of ammonia in sodium hydroxide solution with sodium hypochlorite.

$$2NH_3 + OCl^- \rightarrow NH_2-NH_2 + H_2O + Cl^-$$

Chloramine ($ClNH_2$) is detected in the reaction mixture and it can be shown by independent experiment that ammonia reacts with chloramine to form hydrazine. A side reaction leads to formation of N_2. Formulate reasonable mechanisms for these reactions. Free radical chain mechanisms have been suggested for the reaction, but the evidence against such mechanisms is strong and they need not be considered in your discussion.

5. Whereas NCl_3 hydrolyzes rapidly to give hypochlorous acid and am-

monia, the structurally analogous compound PCl_3 hydrolyzes very rapidly in water to form HCl and phosphorous acid.

$$NCl_3 + 3H_2O \rightarrow NH_3 + 3HOCl$$
$$PCl_3 + 3H_2O \rightarrow P(OH)_3 + 3HCl$$

What implication do you draw from these observations?

6. How do you account for the fact that tetramethylphosphonium salts, $[(CH_3)_4P]^+[X]^-$, exchange protons much more readily than the analogous tetramethylammonium salts?

7. Predict the products of the reaction between ammonia and difluoramine.

8. Oxidation of nitrite ion by hypochlorous acid gives nitrate ion and hydrochloric acid. The rate law has been found to be

$$Rate = k[HOCl][NO_2^-]$$

Formulate a likely mechanism for the reaction.

XIII

Reactivity Correlations

It is reasonable to expect that there should be similarities between reactions which are mechanistically similar, yet it took a long time for this idea to be appreciated. In recent years, extensive correlations of reactivity data have appeared; such correlations are manifestations of linear free energy relations. The underlying theory and assumptions that are inherent in linear free energy relations have been alluded to earlier (Chapter 9, Exercise 7).[1]

13-1 THE NATURE OF CORRELATIONS

At this point we should ask just what is correlated with what? Suppose we take a given substrate and react it with a variety of related reagents which act as *entering groups* in a substitution reaction; an example might be the reaction of methyl bromide with nucleophiles:

---

[1] See also the discussion in J. O. Edwards, *Inorganic Reaction Mechanisms*, Chapter 3, W. A. Benjamin, Inc., New York, 1964.

$$CH_3Br + Nu^- \xrightarrow{k} CH_3\text{---}Nu + Br^- \qquad (13\text{--}1)$$
Methyl
bromide

Appropriate experimental data would consist of the measured rate constants. Now suppose the experiments are repeated using the same nucleophiles and ethyl bromide (CH_3CH_2Br) as substrate. A new set of rate constants, k', will be obtained. Since both sets of reactions are expected to be mechanistically similar, we expect to find a correlation between the k and the k' values.

Alternatively, we might want to use only a single substrate and try to correlate the rate constants with some other property of the nucleophile such as basicity towards the proton.

$$H^+ + Nu^- \xrightleftharpoons{K} H\text{---}Nu \qquad (13\text{--}2)$$

Some chemists have thought it nonsensical to hope for any correlation between kinetic data and thermodynamic data; nevertheless, in many cases excellent correlations do exist. We also hope that it may be possible to take correlation data obtained and transfer it to other systems. An example might be the attack of nucleophiles on N-haloamines:

$$R_2N\text{---}Br + Nu^- \xrightarrow{k''} R_2N\text{---}Nu + Br^- \qquad (13\text{--}3)$$

Transferal of correlation data to other systems, however, can sometimes be hazardous if the possibility exists that these systems may react by a different mechanism. In the above case, we would obtain confusing results if we blindly assumed that all nucleophiles attack nitrogen of the bromoamines, because in fact bromine is usually the site of the attack.

It happens that K [Equation (13-2)] for a nucleophile is not a unique parameter to use in correlation with rate constants if a wide spectrum of nucleophiles is examined. We must either confine an investigation to a sufficiently narrow field or else conclude that other effects besides proton basicity are important. The deviations we observe usually form an underlying pattern; this pattern can then be tested by trying another system that might be expected to behave similarly.

13–2 SPECIFIC EXAMPLES OF CORRELATION: THE SWAIN–SCOTT AND EDWARDS EQUATIONS

Swain and Scott looked at many examples of the substitution reaction at a tetrahedral carbon site:

$$\diagdown \!\!\!\!\overset{\diagdown}{\underset{\diagup}{C}}\!\!-X + Nu^- \xrightarrow{k} \overset{\diagdown}{\underset{\diagup}{C}}\!\!-Nu + X^- \tag{13-4}$$

and found that hundreds of rate constants could be correlated by means of the equation

$$\log\left(\frac{k}{k_0}\right) = s(n) \tag{13-5}$$

In this equation k is a measured rate constant, k_0 is a rate constant for some arbitrary standard reaction, s is a parameter describing the "sensitivity" (or the tendency for reaction) of the substrate, and n is a nucleophilicity parameter describing the reactivity of a nucleophile toward all substrates. The reference reaction which was used to define the origin of the s and n scales was the hydrolysis of methyl bromide for which water was assigned a value of $n = 0$ and methyl bromide a value of $s = 1$. Although universality of application was hoped for, this was not achieved. Nevertheless, the success of Equation (13–5) is indeed remarkable.

In Table 13–1 are collected some n values for various nucleophiles.

Suppose we see just how well these n values correlate with basicity. Table 13–2 lists the appropriate pK values of the conjugate acids.

Comparison of the two tables reveals that correlation is poor. Selected points appear to follow a reasonable trend. For example, with all of the nucleophiles in which the attacking end is an oxygen atom (OH^-, CH_3COO^-, H_2O), there is a regular increase of the n for the nucleophile as the values of pK for the conjugate acid decrease.

Obviously we must now look at the data and see if they can suggest a candidate for an additional factor. Comparison of the n and the pK values for I^- and OH^- suggests that polarizability might play an

TABLE 13-1

Swain–Scott n Values for Various Nucleophiles

Nucleophile	n	Nucleophile	n
$S_2O_3^{2-}$	6.36	Br^-	3.89
I^-	5.04	Cl^-	3.04
SCN^-	4.77	CH_3COO^-	2.72
$C_6H_5NH_2$	4.49	H_2O	0
OH^-	4.20	F^-	<0

important role in determining nucleophilicity. We might just as easily have picked "bulkiness" as the key factor. We shall reject this, however, because if our model (see Figure 13-1) for the transition state in Equation (13-4) is good, then I^- would not be predicted to be more nucleophilic than OH^- merely because the former is larger. In fact, it is well known that if other factors are kept approximately constant, increasing the bulkiness of nucleophiles decreases their reactivity along an associative pathway (see Chapter 14).

TABLE 13-2

pK Values of the Conjugate Acids

Conjugate acid	pK	Conjugate acid	pK
$HS_2O_3^-$	1.9	HBr	-9
HI	-10	HCl	-7
HSCN	-0.7	CH_3COOH	4.7
$C_6H_5NH_3^+$	4.5	H_3O^+	-1.7
H_2O	15.7	HF	3

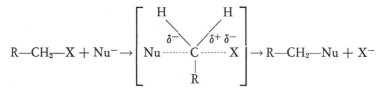

FIGURE 13-1 Model for a concerted-associative mechanism for substitution reactions at tetrahedral carbon.

The question now is just how should the factor of polarizability (a) be added into the construction of n? The introduction of a is done on a semiempirical basis; we might hope that polarizability could be satisfactorily introduced as a term which is separable from the pK term. An equation of the form

$$n = f(\mathrm{pK}) + g(a) \tag{13-6}$$

is therefore implied.

Edwards carried this idea through by expanding the Swain–Scott equation to give

$$\log\left(\frac{k}{k_0}\right) = \alpha P + \beta H \tag{13-7}$$

where P is defined as $\log(R_N/R_{H_2O})$ with R representing the molar refraction of nucleophile N, and H is a function of the pK of the conjugate acid. The constants α and β are characteristic of the substrate; as before, k_0 refers to water as the reference nucleophile, for which $P = H = 0$. Molar refraction R has the units of volume and in principle a given material has a definite value of R at a specified temperature, density, and frequency. Debye showed that for a species with no permanent dipole,

$$R = \frac{n^2 - 1}{n^2 + 2}\left(\frac{M}{\rho}\right) \tag{13-8}$$

where n is the index of refraction, M is molecular weight, and ρ is density.[2] The necessary link with polarizability is supplied by the fact that for nonpolar gases the molar refraction is approximately $\frac{4}{3}\pi Na$. In practice the constants α and β will turn out to be functions of the substrate.

13–3   IMPORTANCE OF THE NATURE OF THE SUBSTRATE

We now turn our attention to the substrates themselves. Marked differences in reactivity exists between saturated and unsaturated substrates; in other words, n values for saturated substrates do not transfer to unsaturated ones. Vinyl chloride represents a very modest change in structure in comparison with ethyl chloride, yet the former is extremely unreactive toward nucleophiles in comparison with the latter.

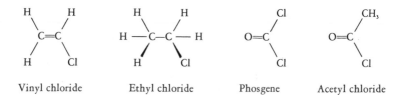

Vinyl chloride   Ethyl chloride   Phosgene   Acetyl chloride

Phosgene and acetyl chloride, by way of contrast, are both very reactive toward nucleophiles. If we presume that both acetyl chloride and vinyl chloride react via an associative mechanism, then the observed substrate reactivity is reasonable because the excess electronic charge in the transition state can be accommodated by the electronegative oxygen atom in the case of acetyl chloride, as shown in Figure 13–2.

---

[2] Only for gases can we accurately express R in terms of density and index of refraction. Application of (13–8) to liquids is done only with some difficulty. Later workers after Debye have refined the expression on the basis of detailed theory. See P. Debye, *Polar Molecules*, The Chemical Catalog Co., New York, 1929.

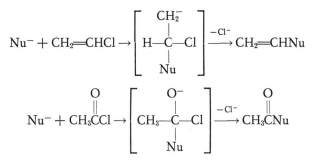

FIGURE 13-2 **Associative pathway for reaction of vinyl chloride and acetyl chloride with nucleophiles.**

This interpretation proves useful because it can be extended to other systems, such as

$$CH_3 \overset{\overset{\displaystyle XR}{\|}}{C} Cl$$

The sluggishness of vinyl chloride suggests that chlorobenzene also ought to be unreactive toward nucleophiles; this prediction is in fact borne out. With a very powerful nucleophile such as amide ion reaction will occur, and is postulated to proceed via the high energy intermediate benzyne. The fact that this

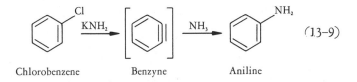

Chlorobenzene   Benzyne   Aniline

(13-9)

course is taken shows that chlorobenzene is unreactive along one of the common substitution pathways. The substance *p*-chloronitrobenzene does react rather readily with many nucleophiles. The intermediate adduct in an associative mechanism is thought to be stabilized by transfer of negative charge to the nitro group, as shown in (13–10).

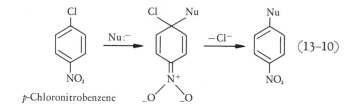

p-Chloronitrobenzene   (13–10)

The mechanisms given in Equations (13–9) and (13–10) are thus quite different.

Suppose we inquire about the other light nonmetallic elements besides carbon. By analogy with carbon we might expect to have attack on nitrogen in nitrosyl chloride; the course of the hydrolysis reaction supports this expectation:

$$O{=}N{-}Cl + H_2O \rightarrow O{=}N{-}OH + HCl \qquad (13{-}11)$$
$$\text{Nitrosyl chloride} \qquad\qquad \text{Nitrous acid}$$

Compare this behavior with that of NCl_3. It is also of interest to consider the substance N-chlorodimethylimine; what can we say about its reactivity relative to that of nitrosyl chloride? By analogy with vinyl chloride the imine should be unreactive. However, attack occurs on the carbon rather than the nitrogen, so a fair comparison cannot be made.

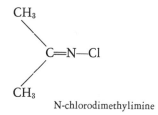

N-chlorodimethylimine

It is interesting to examine what happens as we change the nature of the central atom in the substrate by going down a column in the periodic table. The result of this is quite often a large change in reactivity as a result of a change in mechanism. Phosphorus trichloride reacts with water by a different mechanism than does nitrogen trichloride, presumably because the larger phosphorus can readily increase its coordination number and associative reaction pathways are more probable. This line of reasoning suggests that silicon substrates might be more reactive than analogous carbon compounds. Although we know that CCl_4 is inert to nucleophiles, we predict that $SiCl_4$ should be more reactive; a reasonable mechanism for $SiCl_4$ would be an associative sequence similar to that pictured in Figure 13–2. The prediction agrees with experimental data. Hence, we can conclude that n values for use in a series of saturated carbon substrates should not be transferable to silicon compounds. However, n values obtained from studies of carbon compounds containing multiple bonds:

do a fair job of predicting relative reactivities of nucleophiles toward tetrahedral silicon substrates.

This same sort of conclusion is reached when studying substitution reaction on tetrahedral phosphorus. Studies on methylisopropoxyphosphoryl fluoride reveal that the compound reacts readily with fluoride ion, but is unreactive towards thiosulfate ion, a complete reversal of the relative reactivities of the two nucleophiles toward saturated carbon compounds (see Table 13–1).

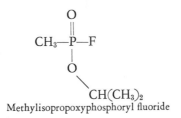

Methylisopropoxyphosphoryl fluoride

13-4   THE CONCEPT OF HARD AND SOFT ACIDS AND BASES

The importance of polarizability as a factor affecting nucleophilicity and substrate sensitivity has been stated compactly in R. G. Pearson's usage of the terms "hard" and "soft" acids and bases. Soft acids and soft bases have *high polarizability* whereas hard acids and bases have *low polarizability*. Consider the general acid-base substitution reaction

$$AB + A'B' \rightleftharpoons AB' + BA'$$

We naturally expect that the strongest base will be coordinated to the strongest acid. However, "strength" and "weakness" of acids and bases are not absolute quantities. The principle of hard and soft acids and bases (HSAB) states that when an acid has a choice between two strong bases, the hard acid will prefer to associate with the harder base, and the soft acid will prefer to associate with the softer base. For example, the very soft acid CH_3Hg^+ forms complexes with both the hard base OH^- and the soft base S^{2-}.

$$CH_3Hg^+ + OH^- \rightleftharpoons CH_3HgOH \qquad pK = -9.4$$
$$CH_3Hg^+ + S^{2-} \rightleftharpoons CH_3HgS^- \qquad pK = -21.2$$

But in competition with H^+ for OH^- and S^{2-}, it is clear that the proton prefers the hard base while CH_3Hg^+ prefers the soft base.

$$H^+ + CH_3HgOH \rightleftharpoons H_2O + CH_3Hg^+ \qquad pK = -6.3$$
$$H^+ + CH_3HgS^- \rightleftharpoons HS^- + CH_3Hg^+ \qquad pK = +8.4$$

The designation of a species as hard or soft comes only after an examination of considerable rate and equilibrium data. Table 13-3 lists some representative hard and soft acids, and Table 13-4 lists some representative hard and soft bases.

The wide range of entries that can be classified in the two tables indicates the general utility of the HSAB principle. Thus, negative

TABLE 13–3

Hard and Soft Acids

Hard		Soft		Borderline
H^+	SO_3	Cu^+	Cs^+	Fe^{2+}
Li^+	Cl^{7+}	Ag^+	Na^0	Cu^{2+}
K^+	I^{7+}	Pd^{2+}	CH_2	SO_2
Ca^{2+}	RCO^+	CH_3Hg^+	Cl,O,N	$B(CH_3)_3$
Fe^{3+}	HCl	I^+	Tl^+	NO^+
BF_3	CO_2	HO^+	Hg^{2+}	Ni^{2+}
RPO_2^+	Mg^{2+}	RO^+	$(CN)_2C{=}C(CN)_2$	RCH_2^+
$ROSO_2^+$	CF_3^+	Cl_2	Pt^{2+}	

standard free energy changes would be predicted for the following reactions using the data in the two tables:

$$HI + AgCl \rightarrow HCl + AgI$$
$$CH_3OH + CH_3OH \rightarrow CH_2(OH)_2 + CH_4$$
$$CH_3HgCl + CH_4 \rightarrow (CH_3)_2Hg + HCl$$

TABLE 13–4

Hard and Soft Bases

Hard		Soft		Borderline
H_2O	ClO_4^-	R_2S	C_2H_4	$C_6H_5NH_2$
OH^-	ROH	RS^-	R^-	C_5H_5N
F^-	RO^-	I^-	$(RO)_3P$	Cl^-
$CH_3CO_2^-$	R_2O	Br^-	R_3P	N_3^-
CO_3^{2-}	NH_3	CO	S^{2-}	
PO_4^{3-}	RNH_2	H^-	C_6H_6	

The nontrivial prediction that the substitution reaction

$$(CH_3)_4N^+ + PR_3 \rightleftharpoons R_3PCH_3^+ + (CH_3)_3N$$

should also occur follows readily in spite of the fact that amines are generally stronger bases toward the proton than are the analogous phosphines.

A second HSAB principle which can be discerned from an inspection of available data is that in a complex consisting of a central atom coordinated by several ligands (bases), extra stabilization is gained if all of the ligands are hard or if all are soft. This can immediately be generalized to include cases where the complex is a transition state. Thus, in the five-coordinate transition state pictured for the associative mechanism (see Figure 13-1), the entering group Nu^- and the leaving group X represent two ligands bound to a central carbon atom. From the statement of the second HSAB principle, we can deduce that the rate constant ratio k_{ROTS}/k_{RI} should be large for hard nucleophiles such as OCH_3^- and $(C_2H_5)_3N$ and small for soft nucleophiles such as $C_6H_5S^-$ and $SeCN^-$, since I^- is a soft base while OTs^-

$$OTs^- = CH_3-\!\!\!\bigcirc\!\!\!-SO_3^-$$

is a hard base. This prediction is borne out by experimental findings.

EXERCISES

1. The Swain–Scott s value for benzoyl chloride is 1.43. Estimate how much faster the reaction

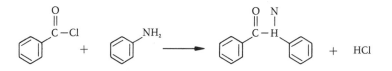

will occur than the hydrolysis of methyl bromide.

2. From what you know about the associative mechanism, can you suggest a reason why pyridine (C_5H_5N) is six times as reactive as triethylamine toward isopropyl iodide [$(CH_3)_2CH$—I] even through the Swain-Scott n values suggest that triethylamine should be at least 25 times *more* reactive than pyridine?

3. If in the transition state in an associative mechanism involving several nucleophiles with a given substrate, the old bond has been broken to a greater extent than the new one has been formed, would you expect the rates

TABLE 13–5

Compound	Solvent	E_a (kcal mole^{-1})	k (sec^{-1})
$(CH_3)_3C$—Cl	Ethanol	25.97	9.70×10^{-8}
(or t − BuCl)	80% aq. EtOH	23.06	1.73×10^{-6}
	50% aq. EtOH	22.92	3.67×10^{-4}
	Methanol	25.0	8.20×10^{-7}
	Water	—	3.3×10^{-2}
	Formic acid	22.9	1.1×10^{-3}
	80% aq. acetone	22.6	1.94×10^{-6}
$(CH_3)_3C$—Br	Ethanol	23.0	5.69×10^{-6}
	80% aq. EtOH	22.8	3.63×10^{-4}
	80% aq. acetone	20.8	1.10×10^{-4}
$CH_3CHCCH{=}CH_2$	Ethanol	23.5	8.8×10^{-9}
|	50% aq. EtOH	—	1.14×10^{-5}
Cl	Water	23.5	8.1×10^{-4}
$(CH_3)_3CCH_2$—Br	50% aq. EtOH	29.0	9.20×10^{-7}
	Formic acid	—	1.53×10^{-6}
$(C_6H_5)_2CH$—Cl	Ethanol	—	5.30×10^{-5}
	80% aq. EtOH	—	1.72×10^{-3}
	80% aq. acetone	21.0	7.24×10^{-5}
$C_6H_5CHCH_3$	Ethanol	21.9	5.85×10^{-7}
|	80% aq. EtOH	21.4	1.64×10^{-4}
Cl	Methanol	21.7	7.06×10^{-6}
	80% aq. acetone	21.8	1.44×10^{-6}

of reaction to be more closely correlated with the P value or the H value of the Edwards equation?

4. Table 13–5 below lists data obtained for the solvolysis of alkyl halides in several protonic solvents (HA). A dissociative mechanism is presumed:

$$R - X \rightarrow R^+ + X^-$$
$$R^+ + HA \rightarrow R - A + H^+$$

(a) Make plots of log k versus log $k^{t-\text{BuCl}}$ for the solvents. What do the linear plots tell you?

(b) By setting the solvolysis of t-butyl chloride in 80% aqueous ethanol as the reference point in correlation scales, show that the data of part (a) may be correlated by means of the equation

$$\log\left(\frac{k}{k_0}\right) = mY$$

where m is a constant characteristic of the substrate, and Y is a constant characteristic of the solvent. Note the similarity in form to the Swain–Scott equation.

(c) Calculate Y values for ethanol and for water. These Y values are supposed to be a measure of "solvent polarity," that is, the more "polar" solvent more easily facilitates separation of charge.

(d) Table 13–6 below is an extensive list of Y values as obtained by Grunwald and Winstein.

Investigate and see if any reasonable correlation exists between these data and either the dielectric constants of the solvents or the dipole moments of the solvent molecules.

(e) On what basis can you infer that *differences* in rates are governed largely by entropy changes?

5. Table 13–7 below gives data for associative substitution reactions on p-nitrophenyl acetate and methylisopropoxyphosphoryl fluoride.

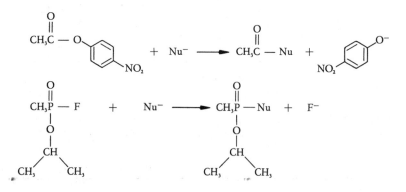

TABLE 13–6

Solvent	Y	Solvent	Y
Ethanol	−2.033	t-Butanol	−3.26
Water	3.493	Formic acid	2.054
Methanol	−1.090	Acetic acid	−1.639
i-Propanol	−2.73	Formamide	0.604

(a) Ascertain whether any reasonable correlation exists between attack at carbon and attack at phosphorus, and between rates and proton basicity.

(b) Thiophenoxide ion ($C_6H_5S^-$) reacts with the phosphorus substrate with a rate constant of 7.4×10^{-3} liter mole^{-1} minute^{-1}. Estimate its rate with the carbon substrate. Likewise, pyridine reacts with the carbon substrate with a rate constant of 0.10 liter mole^{-1} minute^{-1}. Estimate its rate with the phosphorus substrate.

6. With reference to the Edwards equation, would you expect hard acids to have large values of β or of α?

7. Would you expect to find low polarizability associated with high ionization potential or low ionization potential? With small size or large

TABLE 13–7

Nucleophile	pK	k_C (liter mole^{-1} min^{-1})	k_P (liter mole^{-1} min^{-1})
HOO$^-$	11.5	2×10^5	1.0×10^5
Salicylaldoximate	9.2	3.2×10^3	1.5×10^3
OH$^-$	15.7	9×10^2	1.6×10^3
$C_6H_5O^-$	10.0	1×10^2	34
NH_2OH	6	1×10^2	1.3
OCl$^-$	7.2	1.6×10^3	7×10^2
CO_3^{2-}	10.4	1.0	75
H_2O	−1.7	6×10^{-7}	1×10^{-6}

size? With low positive oxidation state or high positive oxidation state (acids)?

8. Predict the direction of reaction in the following systems:

(a) $Mg(CH_3)_2 + 2H_2O \rightleftharpoons Mg(OH)_2 + 2CH_4$

(b) $Co(NH_3)_5F^{2+} + I^- \rightleftharpoons Co(NH_3)_5I^{2+} + F^-$

(c) $CH_3HgCl + HI \rightleftharpoons CH_3HgI + HCl$

(d) $Pt(NH_3)_3Cl^+ + I^- \rightleftharpoons Pt(NH_3)_3I^+ + Cl^-$

XIV

Substitution Reactions of Complexes of Metal Ions

14-1 INTRODUCTION

Previous chapters have emphasized the reaction pathways employed by nonmetallic central atoms in the course of substitution processes. We shall now consider in detail the substitution reactions of metallic central ions as given by Equation (14-1):

$$ML_nX + Y \rightleftharpoons ML_nY + X \qquad (14\text{-}1)$$

No charge is written explicitly for the substrate ML_nX since this can, in principle, be negatively charged, neutral, or positively charged. The central metal atom M plus the most firmly bound ligands (L_n and X) make up an aggregate species called an inner sphere complex; Y is the entering group and X is the leaving group. Molecules in contact with the inner sphere complex are potential entering groups and are said to be in the first "outer sphere" environment. Thus, the $Co(NH_3)_6^{3+}$ ion in aqueous solution may be depicted as shown in Figure 14-1.

The concepts of inner and outer coordination spheres are very useful in considering the details of substitution mechanisms at metal ions.

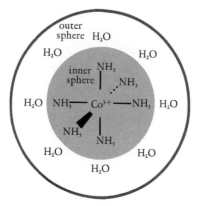

FIGURE 14-1 Model of the inner and outer coordination spheres for the $Co(NH_3)_6^{3+}$ complex in aqueous solution.

14-2 OVERALL LOOK AT METAL ION RATES

Metal ions in aqueous solution may be placed into four classes based on the magnitudes of rate constants for substitutional processes involving complexes of these ions. The portion of the periodic table represented by the ions in each class is shown in Figure 14-2. In the ensuing discussion we shall often be concerned with reactions where $X = H_2O$, the solvent is water, and $L_n = (H_2O)_n$. The four categories as differentiated in Figure (14-2) are defined as follows:

Class I   Exchange of water bound to the metal ion is very fast and essentially diffusion controlled; conventional kinetic techniques are not applicable. First order rate constants are of the order $10^8 \, \text{sec}^{-1}$ or greater. Included in this group are the alkali metal ions and the alkaline-earth metal ions except Mg^{2+} and Be^{2+}.

Class II   The first order rate constant for water exchange is 10^4–$10^8 \, \text{sec}^{-1}$; the dipositive transition metal ions plus the tripositive rare earth ions are in this class, along with Mg^{2+}.

Class III First order rate constants here are $1–10^4$ sec^{-1}. The tripositive transition metal ion Fe^{3+}, plus Be^{2+} and Al^{3+}, are in this class.

Class IV Complexes of Class IV ions are relatively inert; first order rate constants are commonly $10^{-3}–10^{-6}$ sec^{-1} and may be as low as 10^{-9} sec^{-1}. Prominent members include Co^{3+}, Cr^{3+}, and Pt^{2+}.

We should first like to understand in a crude sense the enormous differences in reactivities represented by the four classes, before turning to finer mechanistic considerations. After all, the fact that $K(H_2O)_x{}^+$ undergoes substitution some 10^{15} times faster than $Cr(H_2O)_6{}^{3+}$ can hardly be ignored!

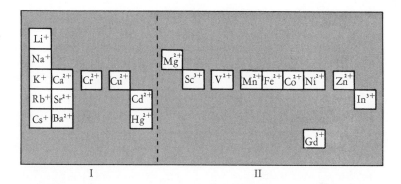

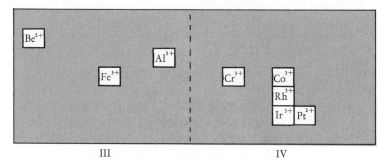

FIGURE 14–2 Classification of metal ions according to rates of ligand substitution reactions. Class I ions react most rapidly, Class II next, and so on.

The simple concepts of the size and positive charge of the metal ions allow us to make much headway. We should expect in the absence of any *specific* electronic structural stabilization that there should be a good correlation between rate constants and the ion charge/size ratio. Small cations have low polarizabilities and consequently should bind hard inner sphere ligands such as water most firmly. And, other factors being equal, the higher the metal ion positive charge, the stronger the binding is expected to be. These concepts explain the fact that Class I is made up of *all* the monopositive and several large dipositive ions. Class II is composed mainly of the smaller dipositive ions and several large tripositive ones. Class III contains the very small Be^{2+} and two small tripositive ions, Fe^{3+} and Al^{3+}. The very low reactivity of the Class IV ions cannot be understood in terms of this simple model, and neither can we explain the fact that the dipositive transition metal ions appear in all classes.

We look to ligand-field theory to help us through the correlation. And, indeed, we see that the Class IV ions have d-electron configurations that give particularly stable ground states in either the octahedral (ML_6) or square-planar (ML_4) structure. The best ground-state electronic structures are d^3 and d^6 (low spin) for octahedral coordination; Cr^{3+} is d^3 and Co^{3+}, Rh^{3+}, and Ir^{3+} are d^6. The square-planar structure prefers the d^8 low-spin ground state, and Pt^{2+} is d^8.

The gross correlation of reactivity and structure is now complete. The idea of charge/size ratio plus a consideration of specially stable ground-state d^n electronic structures allow us to understand the overall substitutional reactivity behavior of the metallic ions. We shall not try to press our luck further, however, until we have examined the *mechanistic* patterns employed by octahedral and square-planar substrates.

14–3 A CLOSER LOOK AT THE ENERGETICS INVOLVED IN DISSOCIATIVE AND ASSOCIATIVE MECHANISMS

We have previously studied simple associative and dissociative pathways for reactions of compounds of nonmetallic elements. The concept of "mode of activation" is particularly useful in the case of metal ion substitutions. For example, if the activation energy is *determined* by the requirements of breaking the bond between the metal and the leaving group, then the rate shows no dependence on the nature of the entering group; this reaction is then said to have a *dissociative* mode of activation. This designation is made because dissociative modes of activation imply that the transition state has no meaningful bond between M and Y, and if a stable intermediate can be isolated it will be expected to have *reduced* coordination number as a result of dissociation of the leaving group. Figure 14–3 depicts the potential energy profile to be expected for this *dissociative* pathway.

Reactions in which the entering group affects the rate of reaction all involve some kind of associative mechanism. If substitution is a single, elementary process, with bond making and breaking occurring simultaneously, the mechanism may be called *concerted-associative*, or

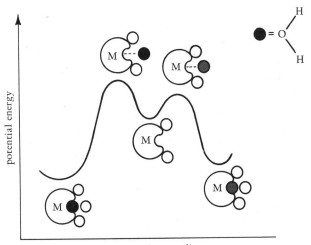

FIGURE 14–3   Potential energy profile for a dissociative mechanism.

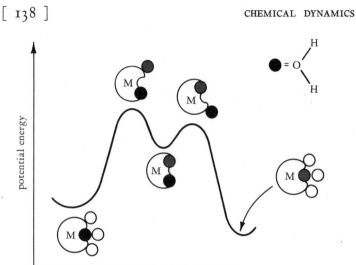

FIGURE 14-4   Potential energy profile for an associative mechanism.

sometimes just *concerted*. A mechanism in which the entering group first adds to the substrate to form an intermediate, which then decomposes to form products, is called *associative*. Examples of both mechanisms were encountered in the earlier chapters. The potential energy profile for a reaction by an associative mechanism, which is common with square-planar Pt(II) complexes, is shown in Figure 14-4.

Kinetic measurements indicate that complexes of Class I and II ions probably undergo substitution via a dissociative mode of activation since the nature of Y has little effect on the rate. Class III complexes do show an entering group dependence and thus some associative activation is indicated; there is, in fact, a correlation between rates in this group and the basicity of the nucleophile Y. Class IV complexes may show either dissociative or associative behavior. They have been extensively studied because they react at conveniently measurable rates; we shall now explore this subject.

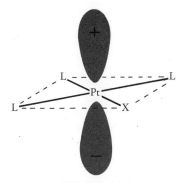

FIGURE 14-5

14-4 LIGAND SUBSTITUTION DYNAMICS IN SQUARE-PLANAR COMPLEXES

Of those Class IV complexes which show associative behavior, the most notable are the Pt(II) complexes. It may be recalled that Pt(II) forms square-planar complexes; since the $6p_z$ platinum orbital, which is oriented perpendicular to the plane of the four ligands, is not involved in strong σ bonding, it is available for forming an extra σ bond required by a five-coordinate transition state in the associative mechanism[1] (see Figure 14-5).

Using a simple electron-repulsion approach, it is seen that a likely intermediate in square-planar substitutions proceeding by an associative mechanism is the trigonal-bipyramidal structure (see Figure 14-6).

The credibility of this statement is strengthened by the fact that in a very few instances compounds analogous to the proposed tri-

---

[1] For a discussion of bonding in square-planar complexes see H. B. Gray and G. P. Haight, Jr., *Basic Principles of Chemistry*, pp. 418–421, W. A. Benjamin, Inc., New York, 1967.

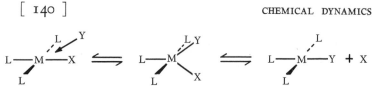

FIGURE 14-6 Associative mechanism for a square-planar substitution.

gonal-bipyramidal intermediates have actually been isolated and characterized. The synthesis of salts of five-coordinated Pt^{2+} anions containing only monodentate ligands has led to the isolation of compounds containing the ions $Pt(SnCl_3)_5^{3-}$, $PtH(SnCl_3)_4^{3-}$, and $Pt(PEt_3)_2 H(SnCl_3)_2^-$ (see Figure 14-7).

Let us now see what the kinetic investigations of square-planar substitution reactions reveal. Experimentally, it is found that the rate law has the following form:

$$\text{Rate} = (k_1 + k_2[Y])[\text{Substrate}] \qquad (14\text{-}2)$$

The second order k_2 term is what one would expect for an associative mechanism. All evidence indicates that the k_1 first order term does not arise from a concurrent dissociative process but rather another associative process involving the solvent. The constant k_2 depends strongly on the nature of Y. Table 14-1 gives values of k_2 for various

TABLE 14-1

**Second Order Rate Data for Reactions of
trans-Pt(pip)$_2$Cl$_2$**

Y	$k_2 \times 10^3$ (*liters mole^{-1} sec^{-1}*)
Cl$^-$	0.9
Br$^-$	6.9
SCN$^-$	400
SeCN$^-$	3300
SC(NH$_2$)$_2$	4600

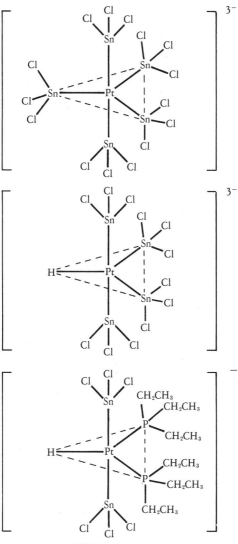

FIGURE 14-7

entering groups Y acting on *trans*-dichlorodipiperidineplatinum(II)
in ethanol at 30°C:

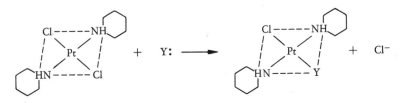

It is also found experimentally that the rate depends on the nature
of the leaving group. This, however, is consistent with either an
associative or a dissociative mechanism. If Y is held constant, a
typical set of k values which emerges is given in Table 14–2.

The reactivity of Pt(II) substrates is modified considerably when
the ligand trans to the leaving group is varied. This effect was
recognized even in the time of Werner and was later explored in detail
in the 1920's by the Russian chemist Chernyaev. We may define the
trans effect as the effect of a coordinated group upon the lability, that

TABLE 14–2

First Order Rate Data for the Reaction[a]

$$Pt(dien)X^+ + C_5H_5N \rightarrow$$
$$Pt(dien)(C_5H_5N)^{2+} + X^-$$

X	$k \times 10^6$ (sec^{-1})
Cl^-	35
Br^-	23
I^-	10
N_3^-	0.83
SCN^-	0.3
NO_2^-	0.050

[a] The abbreviation dien = diethylenetriamine =
$NH_2CH_2CH_2NHCH_2CH_2NH_2$.

is, the rate of substitution, of a ligand trans to it in a metal complex. Although the effect is known to occur in both square-planar and octahedral systems, most of our information is derived from the former, and those *mainly* from Pt(II) systems. Figure (14–8) gives a rough listing of the trans effect order of some common ligands; it will be noted that the relative rates span several orders of magnitude.

As we might expect for such a large rate effect, there are several electronic structural theories concerning its origin. According to the π bonding theory the trans labilizing order parallels the order of the π-electron accepting ability of the labilizing ligand. This was reasoned on the basis of the idea that upon forming the trigonal-bipyramidal intermediate from the square-planar structure, *four* rather than three of the occupied d orbitals would now have the proper symmetry for π-interaction with ligands. A trans group with empty, reasonably stable π orbitals would then lower the energy of the transition state simply by accommodating the excess electronic charge around the central metal atom due to the entering ligand. This type of bonding is shown in Figure 14–9 with CN^- as an example of an acceptor ligand.

The recent finding that ligands such as PR_3, H^-, and CH_3^- are good trans labilizing ligands suggests that factors other than π bonding are also of great importance. Examination of the list of soft bases in the previous chapter reveals that these three ligands are all soft; therefore, it appears that an additional factor which may be at play in trans labilization is related to polarizability. One interpretation is that the positive charge on Pt(II) induces a dipole in the trans labilizing ligand, and this in turn *induces* a dipole in the metal. This induced dipole will be oriented in such a way as to repel nega-

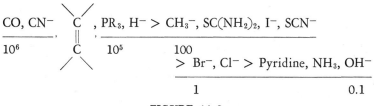

FIGURE 14–8

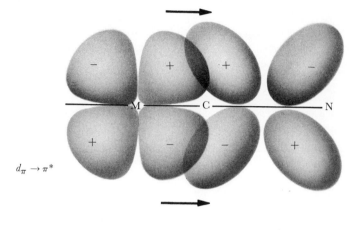

$d_\pi \to \pi^*$

(c)

FIGURE 14-9 π **Bonding between CN$^-$ and a metal d_π orbital.**

tive charge in the leaving group.   Thereby, the binding of the leaving group for Pt(II) will be weakened, making it easier to reach the transition state.   Hence, on the basis of polarizability a trans labilizing order of $PR_3 \sim H^- \sim CH_3^- \sim I^- > Cl^- > OH^-$ is interpretable.

A more sophisticated way of putting it would be in terms of a σ molecular orbital model.   If the trans group has strong σ-interaction with the metal valence $6p$ orbital, then the bond to the leaving group may be relatively weaker in the ground state.   In the transition state the leaving and entering groups now share the previously unoccupied $6p_z$ orbital; the driving force of the reaction is provided by the tendency of the trans ligand to bind as much of the $6p$ orbital as possible by moving the leaving group out of the region of strong overlap.   Because of the large size of the Pt(II) $6p$ orbitals, this model predicts that ligands possessing relatively expanded, σ donor orbitals should exert strong trans effects; this is in good agreement with observation (see Figure 14-10).

The two trans labilizing effects arise from quite different changes in the energy profile for the reaction.   The π-mechanism will actually

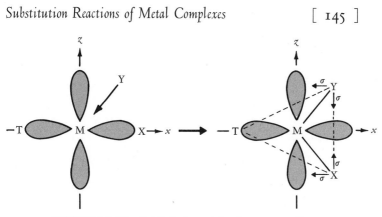

FIGURE 14–10   Orbital changes in the σ trans effect.

lower the energies of both the ground state molecules and the transition states, but the effect is largest in the transition state. The σ-mechanism will tend to raise the energy of both states, but the predominant effect will be in raising the energy of the ground state, by weakening the Pt—X bond. In either case, the activation energy required to produce a transition state is *reduced* as shown in Figure 14–11.

Interesting steric effects are observed in square-planar substitution reactions. A first order rate constant (k_1) for reaction of Pd(dien)Cl$^+$ is typically of the order of 10 sec^{-1}; the value of k_2 is found to depend on the nature of Y. When the terminal amino hydrogens of dien are replaced by ethyl groups, however, the bulkier complex undergoes first order substitution at a considerably slower rate; the value of k_1 drops to about 10^{-3} sec^{-1} for Pd(Et$_4$dien)Cl$^+$.

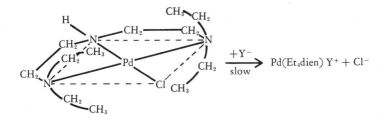

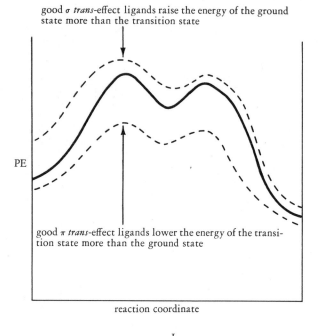

good σ *trans*-effect ligands raise the energy of the ground state more than the transition state

PE

good π *trans*-effect ligands lower the energy of the transition state more than the ground state

reaction coordinate

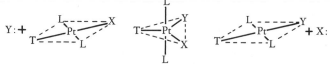

FIGURE 14–11   Energetics of the trans effect by σ- and π-mechanisms.

In very bulky square-planar complexes there may then be a major contribution from a dissociative pathway; the value of 10^{-3} sec^{-1} just given appears to be the magnitude of this contribution, so that for uncrowded complexes essentially all reaction proceeds through the *associative* route.

An interesting trend in values for k_2 is observed when we compare analogous reactions for square-planar complexes containing different

d^8 central metal ions. Orders of magnitude for four such metal ions are as follows:

Metal ion	k_2 (relative)
Ni^{2+}	10^7
Pd^{2+}	10^5
Pt^{2+}	1
Au^{3+}	10^3

For the three dipositive metal ions the rates go down as the metal becomes heavier. This is an interesting contrast to the observations in nonmetallic substitutions, for example, P versus N. Also, Au(III) seems to be anomalous because it reacts much faster than the isoelectronic Pt(II). Again we appeal to ligand-field theory and find that the spectroscopic splitting parameter Δ also follows the order $Ni^{2+} < Pd^{2+} < Pt^{2+} > Au^{3+}$. It is fairly well established now that the magnitude of the ligand-field splitting is related to the strength of covalent binding of ligands to metal d orbitals, which itself is a quantity which should be related to lability.

14–5 LIGAND SUBSTITUTION DYNAMICS IN OCTAHEDRAL COMPLEXES

Complexes of Co(III), another member of Class IV metal ions, have been studied as extensively as those of Pt(II). If the latter provide a good model for associative, square-planar substitution reactions, then the former should provide a good model for *dissociative* activation in octahedral substitution reactions. In octahedral complexes the metal ion makes complete use of its valence p orbitals in σ bonding so that there is no available, empty p orbital for an entering group to bind. This plus the steric problem of disposing

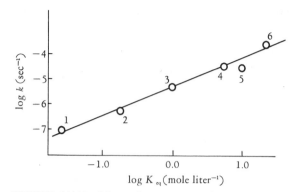

FIGURE 14–12 Linear free energy relation observed
for the hydrolysis of $Co(NH_3)_5X^{2+}$ ions at 25°. The leaving groups, X^-, are: (1), F^-; (2), $H_2PO_4^-$; (3), Cl^-; (4),
Br^-; (5), I^-; and (6), NO_3^-.

seven groups about one atom make an associative mechanism rather
unlikely.[2]

Several experimental pieces of evidence are available which demon-
strate that Co(III) and Pt(II) complexes employ different modes of
activation in their substitution mechanisms. Consider the reaction

$$Co(NH_3)_5X^{2+} + H_2O \rightleftharpoons Co(NH_3)_5(OH_2)^{3+} + X^- \quad (14\text{--}3)$$

which has a free energy of activation $\Delta G^{\ddagger}$ and a standard free energy
change of $\Delta \tilde{G}^{\circ}$. Experimentally, it is found that data for a variety of
leaving groups X lead to the linear free energy relation

$$\Delta(\Delta G^{\ddagger}) = \beta\Delta(\Delta \tilde{G}^{\circ}) \quad (14\text{--}4)$$

with $\beta = 1.0$. In Figure 14–12 is presented a plot of log(rate constant) versus log(equilibrium constant) for the reaction of Equation
(14–3). As the leaving anion is varied, the only significant change
in the overall reaction is the change in the solvated anion produced
as a product. The linear free energy relation with β near 1.0 im-

[2] It should be remarked, however, that examples of seven-, eight-, and nine-coordina-
tion are known, but with metal ions larger than Co(III).

TABLE 14–3

First Order Rate Data for the Reaction[a]

trans-[Rh(en)$_2$Cl$_2$]$^+$ + 2Y → trans-[Rh(en)$_2$Y$_2$]$^{n+}$ + Cl$^-$

Y	$k \times 10^5$ (sec^{-1})
I$^-$ (0.1M)	5.2
OH$^-$ (0.1M)	5.1
SC(NH$_2$)$_2$ (0.1M)	4.9
NO$_2^-$ (0.1M)	4.2
NO$_2^-$ (0.05M)	4.2
Cl$^-$ (0.01M)	4.0
NH$_3$ (5.0M)	4.0

[a] The ligand en is ethylenediamine: NH$_2$—CH$_2$CH$_2$—NH$_2$.

plies that the transition state *resembles closely* the product with respect to the variation. It follows that the leaving group must be functioning very nearly as a solvated anion in the transition state; that is, *effective dissociation has occurred.*

It would be expected that in a pathway employing dissociative mode of activation, the rate of reaction should show little or no entering group effect. In Co(III) substitutions, it is a very general result that, excluding OH$^-$, the entering group has no influence on the rate. Rate laws commonly are strictly first order for Co(III) and other inert octahedral complexes. The data in Table 14–3 above, taken from the work of Johnson, Basolo, and Pearson, show excellently the lack of an entering group effect on the rates of substitution in an octahedral Rh(III) complex.

Since in the transition state of a dissociative-type reaction there is considerable rupture of the metal-to-(leaving group) bond, rates should vary significantly as the leaving group is changed. This effect should be more pronounced than in cases of associative modes of activation. The data presented in Figure 14–12 show that a rather modest variation in the nature of the leaving group gives rise to a difference in rate of a factor of 10^3.

TABLE 14–4

Effect of Substrate Charge on the Rate of Substitution of Chloride by Water in Cobalt(III) and Platinum(II) Complexes

Substrate	$k_1(H_2O)$, sec^{-1} $(25°C)$	Ratio, $\dfrac{n+}{(n+1)+}$
$Pt(NH_3)_3Cl^+$	2.6×10^{-5}	3.8
$trans\text{-}Pt(NH_3)_2Cl_2$	9.8×10^{-5}	
$Co(NH_3)_5Cl^{2+}$	6.7×10^{-6}	2.7×10^2
$trans\text{-}Co(NH_3)_4Cl_2^+$	1.8×10^{-3}	

As a final comparison showing the difference in the activation energetics of Pt(II) and Co(III), consider the effect of varying the charge on the substrate. Relevant experimental data are set out in Table 14–4. The fact that the rate depends strongly on the substrate charge only in the Co(III) system shows that the activation energetics are different in the two model systems.

TABLE 14–5

Activation energetics	Influence of:			
	Entering group	Leaving group	Steric crowding	Substrate charge
Associative	Large	Variable	Very large decrease in rate	Generally small
Dissociative	Negligible	Large	Moderate to large increases in rate	Generally large

In conclusion, the models Co(III) and Pt(II) allow us to put forward some useful generalizations concerning relative rates expected for the two different modes of activation. These generalizations are given in Table 14–5.

EXERCISES

1. In addition to the two-step dissociative and associative processes, there are also one-step processes which we have earlier called "concerted" but are also referred to as "interchanges" by workers in the metal ion field.

$$ML_nX + Y \xrightarrow{k_1} ML_nY + X \qquad \text{interchange}$$

$$ML_nX \underset{k_{-2}}{\overset{k_2}{\rightleftharpoons}} ML_n + X \xrightarrow{+Y}{k_3} ML_nY \qquad \text{dissociative}$$

$$ML_nX + Y \underset{k_{-4}}{\overset{k_4}{\rightleftharpoons}} ML_nXY \xrightarrow{k_5} ML_nY + X \qquad \text{associative}$$

What is the molecularity of an interchange reaction? What kind of kinetics do you expect to observe? Discuss how the interchange process might show the activation energetics of (a) an associative mechanism, or (b) a dissociative mechanism.

2. Make the steady state hypothesis and write the general rate law expression for the rate of disappearance of ML_nX in a dissociative reaction. What sort of mechanistic ambiguity may arise if X is a solvent molecule?

3. Make the steady state assumption and write the rate law expression for the rate of disappearance of a complex in an associative reaction. What problem arises if Y is a solvent molecule?

4. Explain why the rate order of water substitution in the alkaline-earth metal ions is $Ca^{2+} > Mg^{2+} > Be^{2+}$.

5. Consider the octahedral complexes $Cr(H_2O)_6^{3+}$, $Cr(H_2O)_5Cl^{2+}$, and $Cr(H_2O)_4Cl_2^+$.
(a) What do you expect for the relative rates of water substitution?
(b) In the chloro-substituted complexes, which reaction is faster, H_2O substitution or Cl^- substitution?
(c) Discuss the probable mechanism of Cl^- substitution.

6. Consider the substrates *trans*-Pt(NH$_3$)$_2$Cl$_2$, *trans*-Pt(NH$_3$)$_2$(Br)Cl, and *trans*-Pt(NH$_3$)$_2$(I)Cl.
(a) In a reaction with labeled Cl^-, which group is replaced most rapidly in each case? Explain.
(b) Compare the reactivity of the three substrates toward $^{36}Cl^-$, I^-, and CN^- as entering groups. Which combination of substrate and entering group should give the fastest reaction?

7. Formulate an explanation of the following rates of water substitution.

	k (sec^{-1})
$Ni(H_2O)_6^{2+}$	2.5×10^4
$Co(H_2O)_6^{2+}$	2×10^5
$Fe(H_2O)_6^{2+}$	3×10^6
$Zn(H_2O)_4^{2+}$	3×10^7
$Cu(H_2O)_6^{2+}$	2×10^8

8. Consider the substrates cis-PtL_2Cl_2 and $trans$-PtL_2Cl_2 with $L = PR_3$ or NH_3.

(a) In a substitution reaction, what would you expect to be the leaving group?

(b) Predict the reactivities of the isomeric substrates.

9. Discuss probable mechanisms and predict relative rates of $^{14}CN^-$ exchange in the complexes $Ni(CN)_4^{2-}$ and $Co(CN)_6^{3-}$.

XV

Lectures on Frontier Areas in
Chemical Dynamics

Although chemical dynamics may be defined simply as the investigation of the rates and mechanisms of the interconversions of species, it must certainly be clear by now that it is an extremely variegated field encompassing quite a wide range of topics for study. In order to gain a better feeling for the specific kinds of problems which chemical dynamicists are pursuing today, it is proposed in this concluding chapter to expose the student to some examples of actual research problems which are currently being pursued. Because the material in each of the sections deals with active projects, it may seem somewhat unfinished and lacking in sound conclusions. In all cases many ramifications remain to be explored before some of these fundamental conclusions can reach daylight.

The four topics presented in this chapter have been arranged in what seems to be a reasonable order of increasing complexity of the system under study. Accordingly, we begin with a case study of a type of reaction which was alluded to earlier (Chapter 6), namely, a crossed molecular beam study of the reaction between alkali metal atoms and alkyl halides in the gas phase. The somewhat simple nature of the system permits a closer scrutiny of the mechanics of the reaction than in the cases to follow.

15-1   CHEMICAL DYNAMICS IN REALLY SIMPLE SYSTEMS

In recent years some theoretical understanding of the rates of chemical reactions has come from a study of some rather simple systems. The gaseous reaction of alkali metals with alkyl halides is such a simple system and is typified by the example below:

$$K \cdot + CH_3\text{---}I \rightarrow KI + CH_3 \cdot \qquad (15\text{-}1)$$

Because the methyl group tends to act as one unit, it is a fair approximation to treat this case as a three-atom collision.

Polanyi and von Hartel studied the case of sodium and methyl iodide. Gaseous sodium in a slowly flowing stream of nitrogen diffuses into a tube containing vaporized methyl iodide (see Figure 15-1).

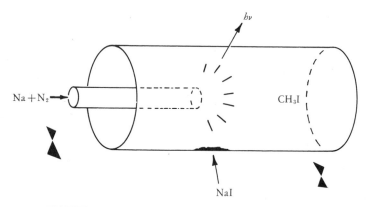

FIGURE 15-1   System used by Polanyi and von Hartel.

Light $(h\nu)$ is emitted with an intensity proportional to the concentration of sodium so that the progress of the reaction can actually be followed by noting the light emitted. From this a rate constant can be obtained, and if we assume a bimolecular mechanism for the reaction, the rate expression is found to be

$$\text{Rate} = \frac{-d(n_{\text{Na}})}{dt} = \frac{d(n_{\text{CH}_3})}{dt} = k n_{\text{Na}} n_{\text{CH}_3\text{I}} \qquad (15\text{-}2)$$

where n_i is the number of molecules of i per cubic centimeter. By studying the reaction at several temperatures we can get some idea of the temperature variation of the rate constant. In the present case an Arrhenius expression is found to fit the data.

$$k = A \exp\left(-\frac{E_a}{kT}\right) \qquad (15\text{-}3)$$

Polanyi and von Hartel interpreted A as a measure of the success of each collision. The activation energy E_a was found to be 0.3 kcal mole^{-1}.

The authors then set up a model to try to explain the results (see Figure 15-2). The model chosen was that of colliding hard spheres; reference has already been made to this model of reaction rate theory (see Chapter 8).

By taking B to be essentially stationary so that the velocity of A is

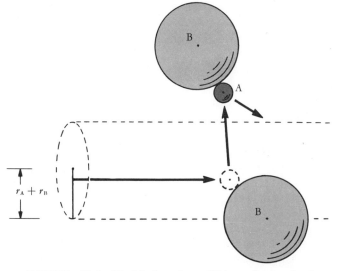

FIGURE 15-2 Model for the collision of two hard spheres.

nearly the relative speed, the following expression for the collision number can be obtained:

$$\text{Collisions cm}^{-3}\,\text{sec}^{-1} = Z_{AB} = \pi(r_A + r_B)^2 v n_B n_A \quad (15\text{-}4)$$

where the r values are appropriate radii of the spheres. The product $\pi(r_A + r_B)^2$ is the area presented by an A to a B molecule or the collision cross section. Not all the molecules have the same relative velocity, so it becomes necessary to consider a Maxwell–Boltzmann distribution of speeds. If P represents the probability of a collision resulting in reaction, Equations (15-2) and (15-3) may be rewritten together as

$$k n_A n_B = Z_{AB} P = \pi(r_A + r_B)^2 v n_A n_B P = A \exp\left(-\frac{E_a}{kT}\right) n_A n_B \quad (15\text{-}5)$$

It is clear than an identification may be made between P and $\exp(-E_a/kT)$ and between $\pi(r_A + r_B)^2\ v$ and A. By taking $(r_A + r_B)^2$ to be 35 Å^2, Polanyi and von Hartel could get reasonable agreement with experiment. It is not possible to work backward unambiguously from results such as these and infer details about the nature of the reaction. It is recalled that one of the earliest triumphs of collision theory was the rationalization of the data of Bodenstein for the $H_2 + I_2$ reaction using an assumed mechanism which, from the recent kinetic work of Sullivan, now seems to be highly suspect.

Let us now consider in detail an isolated single collision (see Figure 15-3).

To do this perpendicular beams of gaseous potassium and vaporized methyl iodide are directed toward each other in a vacuum. This experiment was first done by Herschbach, Kwei, and Norris. In order to collimate the beams, several slits are employed. The vector $\mathbf{v}_{cm}$ represents that expected for the motion of the center of mass of the colliding system. A plot of the number of molecules per second hitting a detector versus the angle α is shown below in Figure 15-4. The potassium iodide is found to come off at an angle significantly greater than that for the center of mass.

How can this be interpreted? If the metal and halide may be presumed to come together to form a transition state of appreciable lifetime, then in order for angular momentum to be conserved, this

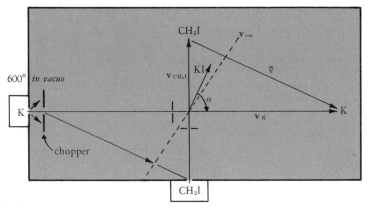

FIGURE 15-3   Crossed-beam experiment.

complex must rotate. The effect would be that KI should be ejected
with a distribution that is symmetric forward and backwards along
the relative velocity vector, **v**. Since this is not observed, we can
rigorously conclude that the complex has a lifetime of the order of
one molecular rotation or less $(< 10^{-12}$ sec). In contrast, reactions
between larger molecules which may be expected to show this symmetric behavior may be referred to as *sticky* collisions. It is an interesting theoretical problem to try to predict whether a collision
will be sticky or not.

Consider Figure 15-5 below (note change of notation: θ is the
scattering angle referred to **v**, α referred to $\mathbf{v}_K$).

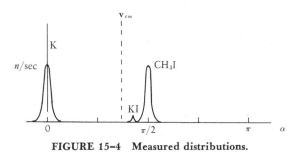

FIGURE 15-4   Measured distributions.

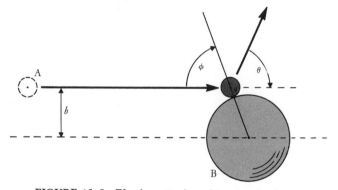

FIGURE 15-5   Elastic scattering of two hard spheres.

The following trigonometric relationship is easily shown:

$$\sin \phi = \frac{b}{r_A + r_B} = \sin \frac{(\pi - \theta)}{2} = \cos \frac{\theta}{2} \qquad (15\text{-}6)$$

The angle θ, to which molecule A is scattered, is a measurable quantity so that knowing it we can get an idea of b, the relative "off-centerness" of the two spheres (assuming, also, that we have available suitable values for r_A and r_b), that is, the extent to which collisions do not occur head-on. The probability of reaction may depend on the magnitude of b. For a small change in b there will correspond a small change $d\theta$ in the angle of scattered product

$$2\pi b db = 2\pi\sigma \sin \theta \, d\theta \qquad (15\text{-}7)$$

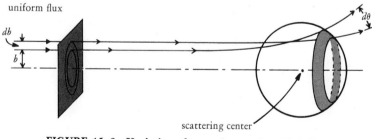

uniform flux

FIGURE 15-6   Variation of scattering angle with b for hard spheres.

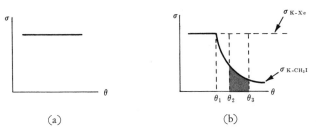

FIGURE 15-7 **Variation of cross section, for the scattering of K atoms, with scattering angle for (a) K + Xe, (b) K + CH₃I.**

where $\sigma = \sigma(v, \theta)$ is the cross section (see Figure 15-6). For colliding hard spheres σ is a constant; using Equations (15-6) and (15-7) the magnitude of this constant works out to be $\frac{1}{4}(r_A + r_B)^2$ so that a plot of σ versus θ gives the result shown in Figure 15-7(a). This condition is approximated in the case of the collision of potassium and xenon atoms when b is relatively small. For large b the attractive forces between molecules produce a marked variation from the hard sphere case.

For the scattering of K atoms by CH₃I a somewhat different looking plot is obtained [see Figure 15-7(a) and (b)]. At θ_1 we have the threshold or smallest angle, corresponding to the largest b, at which the effect of reaction just begins to be noticed; the shaded area indicates how much potassium has disappeared by being transformed to potassium iodide. The probability factor may be estimated from

$$P = \frac{\sigma_{Xe-K} - \sigma_{CH3I-K}}{\sigma_{Xe-K}} \tag{15-8}$$

With this definition of P the experiments show that a plot of P (which is ultimately a function of b) versus b resembles that shown below in Figure 15-8.

This kind of information is interesting to compare with theoretical calculations for reactive collisions. The maximum value of b occurs at about 3.5 Å. Either the area under the KI peak of Figure 15-4 or the shaded area of Figure 15-7(b) represents the amount of KI pro-

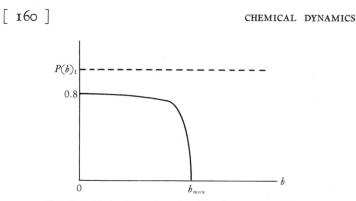

FIGURE 15-8   Plot of probability factor versus b.

duced in the reaction.   For example, using Figure 15-7(b) we can write for the reaction cross section σ_R

$$\sigma_R = \int_0^{b_{max}} P(b)\, db \qquad (15\text{-}9)$$

Both integrations agree in giving $\sigma_R \simeq 30\ \text{Å}^2$.

The hard sphere model is too simple to give a precise picture of a real reaction.   However, it does show many of the qualitative features which are brought out more accurately in fancier models.

Sometimes theoretical models have been forced to fit experimental results by including an arbitrary multiplicative factor, the so-called steric factor.   This procedure is aesthetically unpleasing.   One way to do better is to try to measure the effect of molecule orientation on the reaction cross section; we expect that, other things remaining equal, the probability of reaction occurring ought to depend on how the metal atom and the halide are oriented when they collide. Recent sophisticated experiments (by Brooks and Jones and by Beuhler, Bernstein, and Kramer) have enabled methyl iodide molecules to be beamed in mostly one orientation or another.   The reaction cross sections show a large dependence on orientation.

$$\frac{\sigma_{R\text{CH}_3\text{I}-\text{Rb}}}{\sigma_{R\text{ICH}_3-\text{Rb}}} \gtrsim 1.5 \qquad (15\text{-}10)$$

This kind of experiment is an excellent example of how the details of simple reactions are being studied.

An increasing level of complexity of the system studied is illustrated by the gas phase reaction of atomic carbon ions with various organic substrates, chiefly hydrocarbons, since here a multitude of products can form. It is clear that in this case account must be taken of the presence of an intermediate or intermediates which can pursue paths to several products.

15–2   REACTIONS OF ATOMIC CARBON

In recent years there has been a growing interest in the study of the reactions of atomic carbon. The reason for this is apparently two-fold: first, there is the obvious relevance to the more general study of all carbon-containing systems, that is, reactions of atomic carbon have been chiefly with other carbon-containing molecules. Second, atomic carbon is the last member in the series CH_4, $CH_3\cdot$, $CH_2:$, $\cdot\overset{\cdot\cdot}{C}H$, $\cdot\overset{\cdot\cdot}{C}\cdot$, and thus with reference to methane it is about as electron-deficient as one would imagine. Its chemistry might therefore resemble that of CH_2, for example, but also its extreme deficiency might be responsible for some rather unusual properties.

At least four different methods are known for generating atomic carbon. It can be made in a carbon arc, by photolysis of a mixture of carbon suboxide (C_3O_2) and methane, and by passing carbon monoxide through a plasma of helium. This latter method is inconvenient for chemical purposes; a better method is synthesis by nuclear reactions (see Figure 15–9). In this method a high energy stream of tetrapositive carbon-12 ions are passed through a platinum foil. The majority of the ions pass through unaltered while the remainder emerge as tetrapositive carbon-11 ions. Since carbon-11 is radioactive we now have a built-in tracer which will be useful when studying reaction mechanisms. This beam can then be directed at some material to be bombarded (substrate).

The general procedure is to allow the atomic carbon and the substrate to react and then to take the mixture of products, separate them by means of a very sensitive chromatographic technique, and finally analyze them.

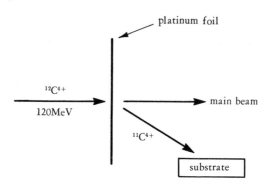

FIGURE 15–9   Synthesis of radioactive atomic carbon.

Notice that in the synthesis of the carbon it is tetrapositive ions, not uncharged particles, that are produced. When passing through the substrate, however, these ions will first have a greater tendency to abstract random electrons rather than enter into chemical combination. Ultimately, then, we need only decide whether a chemical reaction has resulted from unipositive ions or the neutral atoms.

$$C^+ + S \rightarrow C + S^+ \qquad \Delta E_1 \qquad (15\text{–}11)$$

$$C + S \rightarrow C^+ + S + e^- \quad \Delta E_2 \qquad (15\text{–}12)$$

The activation energy for Reaction (15–11) is on the order of 1–2 eV while that for Reaction (15–12) is about 10 eV. This means that at low beam energies Reaction (15–11) will be very important. The carbon atoms so produced are still not normal carbon atoms for although they are in a low energy electronic state, they are nevertheless "hot" atoms in the sense of having an excess of kinetic energy. Any reactions which these atoms undergo are called "hot reactions." By adding a massive amount of inert moderator (such as neon gas) to the substrate much of the excess kinetic energy can be absorbed, and thus the kinetic energy of the atoms more nearly approaches kT; reactions may now be called *thermal* reactions. In studying both hot-atom and thermal reactions it happened that the results were not terribly different. This may possibly be because the carbon atoms possess so much internal energy that any excess translational energy makes very little difference.

To date, the most extensive reactions of atomic carbon which have been investigated have been with hydrocarbons. With ethylene, for example, several products are obtained, including $HC\equiv{}^{11}C{-}H$, $H_2C{=}^{11}C{=}CH_2$, and others. In fact, with many hydrocarbons a good yield of acetylene is almost always obtained; cyclopropane, for example, gives a 60% yield of acetylene. A plausible explanation for some of the products formed from atomic carbon reactions could be that the carbon inserts into a C—H bond; the resulting intermediate then goes on to do chemistry in a variety of ways.

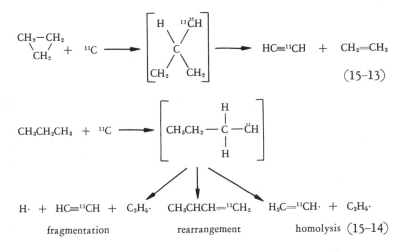

$$(15\text{-}13)$$

$$(15\text{-}14)$$

In order to lend substantial proof to this mechanistic suggestion, ethane was prepared with one methyl group completely deuterated. This would presumably react with atomic carbon via the insertion mechanism as follows:

$$(15\text{-}15)$$

The acetylene was examined by mass spectrometry and it was found that both undeuterated and dideuterated acetylene was present, but no monodeuterated acetylene was present. Thus it appears that one mechanism for reactions of atomic carbon is the insertion into a C—H bond to form an intermediate adduct which can then either stabilize or decompose.

Another plausible mechanism for some atomic carbon reactions is insertion into a C=C bond. This would explain, for example, the formation of allene, centrally-labeled, from ethylene.

$$H_2C{=}CH_2 + {}^{11}C \rightarrow H_2C{=}{}^{11}C{=}CH_2 + \text{Other products} \qquad (15\text{-}16)$$

A third plausible mechanism might also be the abstraction of random hydrogens until CH_2: is formed; this species might then react in its own manner. Note that in the case of the C—H insertion reactions there are two different types of paths which the adduct can follow: a decomposition path and a rearrangement path. It was found experimentally that by increasing the pressure in the gaseous system, or by going to the liquid or solid phase, the rearrangement path could be made to predominate over the decomposition path. This is a general result; the explanation is that in a more condensed medium the excess energy of a reacting species can be lost more conveniently by vibrational decay upon collisions rather than by bond breaking processes.

An interesting reaction of atomic carbon which merits further study is the reaction with a mixture of undeuterated and perdeuterated ethanes. Only four isomeric propenes (in about equal amounts) are formed:

$$\left.\begin{matrix} C_2H_5 \\ C_2D_6 \end{matrix}\right\} + {}^{11}C \rightarrow \begin{cases} C_2{}^{11}CH_6 \\ C_2{}^{11}CH_5D \\ C_2{}^{11}CD_6 \\ C_2{}^{11}CD_5H \end{cases} \qquad (15\text{-}17)$$

If the initial ^{11}C is in a singlet state, then the adduct will be a singlet and will merely rearrange to give undeuterated and perdeuterated propenes. But if the attacking ^{11}C is a triplet, the triplet adduct will be somewhat unstabilized and will tend to decompose by losing a hydrogen atom; abstraction of a hydrogen or deuterium atom from some source would then give additional isomeric propenes.

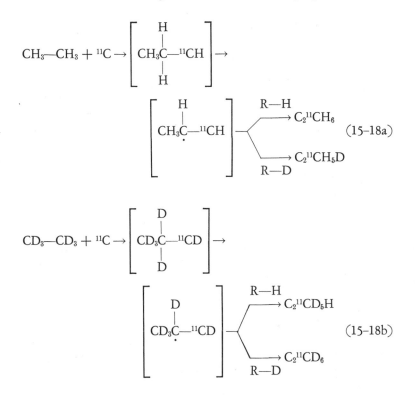

$$(15–18a)$$

$$(15–18b)$$

Additional mechanisms may come to light in further study of the reactions of atomic carbon; ^{11}C may be found to insert into other bonds also, and of course, the question of why ^{11}C inserts into C—H or C=C bonds at all has not really been answered.

Dynamical processes studied in solution can be expected to be even more complex than gas phase reactions since now a truly adequate description of the mechanics of the process would require taking into account the surroundings in addition to the actual reactants. Presently, the medium is taken into account in varying degrees of sophistication, depending on the process under study.

It is also to be expected that certain new techniques will become applicable to solution phase studies which would be impossible or impractical to use in gas phase problems. Nuclear magnetic resonance spectroscopy of processes in *homogeneous* media is one such technique, and by its very nature there is introduced the additional problem of properly describing the interaction of matter with radiation.

15–3 CHEMICAL DYNAMICS AS REVEALED BY NUCLEAR MAGNETIC RESONANCE SPECTROSCOPY

In recent years electron microscopy has been used extensively in the study of large, biological molecules. Use of electron microscopy and of X-ray diffraction is restricted almost entirely to the solid phase. Most processes of interest to the chemist and the biologist occur in solution, however. Since solid phase data usually cannot be transferred to the solution phase, another instrumental method of analysis is obviously required. Nuclear magnetic resonance spectroscopy is ideally suited for the study of the structure and dynamics of organic molecules.

To understand the essence of the magnetic resonance method we should realize that it is just another branch of spectroscopy employing a different region of the electromagnetic spectrum, in this case the radio-frequency region of 3–30 m. At a normal frequency of 60 Mc the size of the quantum amounts to about *6 × 10⁻³ cal mole⁻¹*! Energy of this magnitude will, therefore, only be able to induce transitions between levels that are very closely spaced. Such energy levels in a molecule are in fact those associated with a change in the spin quantum number of a particular nucleus. Certain nuclei of interest to chemists (^{1}H, ^{13}C, ^{15}N, and ^{19}F) act as if they were charged spinning bodies possessing a magnetic moment of $\pm \frac{1}{2} \gamma \hbar / \beta_N$, depending on whether the "nuclear magnets" can be regarded as effectively lined up with the field ($-\frac{1}{2}$) or against the field ($+\frac{1}{2}$). The quantity γ is the gyromagnetic ratio, which is a constant characteristic of a particular kind of nucleus; β_N is the nuclear magneton, and $\hbar$ is Planck's constant divided by 2π. When a sample that is immersed in a constant magnetic field H_0 is irradiated with radio-

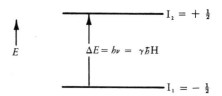

FIGURE 15-10 Energy levels for a single nucleus with a spin of $\frac{1}{2}$ in a magnetic field of strength H.

frequency energy, some of the spins in the more favorable energy state (spin quantum number $-\frac{1}{2}$) are induced to undergo a transition to the less favorable state (see Figure 15-10).

The distribution of spins between the two states follows the Boltzmann law; from what was said earlier regarding the size of the quantum, it is easy to see that the difference in populations between the two levels will be very small.

Fortunately for the chemist not all the protons, for example, in a given molecule will necessarily have the same resonance frequency (ν). This is because magnetic fields are set up by the electrons around a nucleus. Since electron distributions in general are different about each chemically differently located proton, the effective magnetic field which the nucleus "sees" is not H_0 but $H_0(1 - \sigma)$, where σ is a parameter characteristic of a particular type of proton. At the resonance frequency where the proton changes its spin quantum number, the energy change involved will therefore be $\Delta E = \gamma \hbar H_0(1 - \sigma)$. These changes are recorded as a nuclear magnetic resonance spectrum; proton transitions are usually referenced with respect to that observed for tetramethylsilane $[(CH_3)_4Si]$, so that for a proton H^1 in a molecule the relative energy change will be proportional to $(\sigma^0 - \sigma^1)$. When this difference is scaled to give numbers of a suitable magnitude, the result is called the chemical shift of nucleus ^1H relative to the standard.

The value of the chemical shift lies in the fact that it is an analytical probe for very subtle changes in the magnetic environment of nuclei. Let us now take an example and see how nuclear magnetic

resonance spectroscopy can be applied to a specific problem. The
molecule difluorotetrachloroethane can exist as two isomers, I and
II. These are ordinarily not readily interconvertible.

I   II

However, either one of these, say I, can exist in numerous orienta-
tions or conformations, depending on the extent of rotation about the
carbon-carbon single bond. The two conformations of greatest interest are the gauche (Ia) and the trans (Ib) conformations.

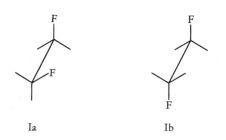

Ia   Ib

It would be interesting to know the proportions of each form which
are present and how rapidly they interconvert (as a function of temperature).

   When an *nmr* spectrum of I is taken at −120°, the result is the spectrum shown in Figure 15–11(a). A nuclear magnetic resonance spectrometer may be likened to a camera, so that apparently the gauche-
trans interconversion is slow enough to be "photographed." In-
tegration of each peak then gives the relative amounts of the two
conformers.[1] In order to find out how fast they interconvert it is

---

[1] It is a more difficult task to determine which peak corresponds to which
conformer.

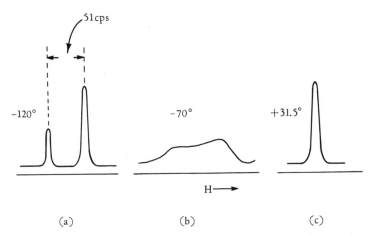

FIGURE 15–11 Temperature dependent spectra of 1,2-difluorotetrachloroethane at 56.4 Mc.

necessary to take spectra at several temperatures. Figures 15–11(b) and 15–11(c) show spectra taken at two higher temperatures. At −70° the two peaks appear as a broad band, which may be likened to a "photographic blur," but is properly explained in terms of the quantum mechanical equations that describe the system. When room temperature is reached Ia and Ib interconvert so rapidly that the magnetic environment of the fluorines becomes averaged and only a single signal appears. From a detailed analysis of the way the line shape changes with temperature it is possible to calculate the rate of interconversion at any desired temperature. Spectral analysis has advanced to the point where this operation is largely computerized.

As another example of great interest consider a disubstituted cyclohexane (III). The atoms bound to the ring carbons divide into two classes, axial and equatorial. The ring skeleton is drawn in the shape of a chair because this form of the molecule minimizes the repulsions occurring between nonbonded atoms. An alternative structure exists in which the ring is shaped like a boat and which is in equilibrium with the chair form. Because the boat form possesses several serious nonbonded repulsions, most equilibrium mixtures of cyclohexanes usually predominantly consist of the chair form.

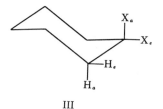

III

If we make a molecular model of III it is found that the ring can "flip" to give another chair form, as shown in Figure 15-12. The effect of this flipping is to convert an axial group (X') into an equatorial group (X) and vice versa. However, X' and X in a given chair form are in different magnetic environments, so that if the interconversion between IIIa and IIIb is slow enough, it ought to be possible to study this process by nuclear magnetic resonance spectroscopy because X' and X should show two separate resonances.

This is indeed the case. In Figure 15-13(a) is shown the spectrum of 1,1-difluorocyclohexane taken at −100°. In principle the ring flipping could also be studied if X and X' were hydrogen; however, the 10 to 50 times greater chemical shift of fluorine with respect to hydrogen makes it more desirable to use the fluorine nucleus as a label. The two sharp signals on the left side of Figure 15-13(a) belong to the equatorial fluorine, while the ones on the right belong to the axial fluorine. In each case two peaks instead of one are seen

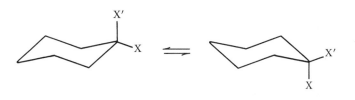

IIIa   IIIb

FIGURE 15-12   Ring flipping of a 1,1-disubstituted cyclohexane.

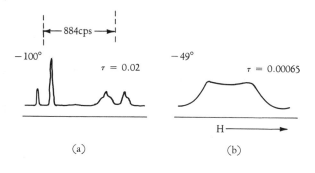

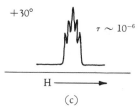

FIGURE 15-13 ¹⁹F spectra of 1,1-difluorocyclohexane at 56.4 Mc.

because of interaction of the magnetic moments of the two fluorine nuclei with each other. The axial signals are broadened by further interaction of the axial fluorine nuclear magnetic moment with the magnetic moments of neighboring hydrogens. These types of inter-actions are referred to as *spin-spin* splitting interactions. Notice also the healthy chemical shift difference of 884 cps between the two types of fluorines.

As the temperature is increased the rate of interconversion of IIIa and IIIb is increased. The values of τ which are given are the mean lifetimes (in seconds) of a state before inversion occurs. The shape of the spectrum at two higher temperatures is given in Figures 15-13(b) and 15-13(c). At room temperature ring inversion is so rapid that again we observe only an averaging of the two fluorines, which appears as a normal quintet due to spin-spin splitting inter-

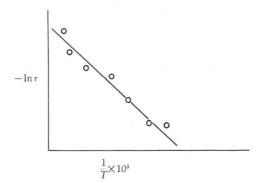

$-\ln \tau$

$\frac{1}{T} \times 10^3$

FIGURE 15–14 Typical plot for obtaining an activation energy for ring inversion.

actions with four neighboring protons. The Arrhenius activation energy E_a (assumed to be temperature-independent over the range of interest) for the ring flipping can be obtained by plotting the logarithm of $1/\tau$ versus reciprocal temperature, as shown below in Figure 15–14. A linear plot is usually obtained, the slope of which is a simple function of E_a.

Interesting variations of this set of experiments can be done by putting substituents at other places in the ring. We expect this to affect the equilibrium constant for a process like IIIa $\rightleftharpoons$ IIIb, where now both possible chair conformers may not necessarily be equal in energy. The observed spectra will now become more complicated, but in a way this is more or less predictable.[2]

In addition, it is an interesting theoretical problem to try and predict how the value of the equilibrium constant changes with the nature of the substituent. The present status of the field is such that this "prediction" is little more than a correlation.

In conclusion what can we say about the value of the nuclear magnetic resonance method? Its importance lies in the fact that it allows processes in solution to be studied. This is most important from a

---

[2] It should be mentioned that, in general, boat forms of cyclohexanes are not observed in *nmr* spectra because of their relatively low concentrations.

biological standpoint since most reactions in the human system involving biologically important species take place in aqueous media. With refined instrumentation it is rapidly becoming possible to look at protein solutions and derive meaningful information. With proteins we expect to be able to observe large changes with temperature due to denaturation effects; this is in fact observed, although the interpretation of these changes is still a difficult problem. Smaller molecules can hopefully act as models for future study of larger molecules.

Among the most difficult processes of all to comprehend are those that occur heterogeneously, that is, at the boundary of two phases. Some familiar examples include solubility processes, the Volta and photoelectric effects, metal catalysis of hydrogenation, the distribution of a solute between two immiscible solvents, and electrode reactions. The latter can be expected to be complex since these processes occur within a few molecular diameters of the surface of the useful electrode, and it is no longer a reasonable approximation to treat the intervening medium as a *continuous* bulk dielectric. A more detailed knowledge of the structure of the solution near the electrode is demanded.

15-4 ELECTROCHEMICAL DYNAMICS

The electrochemical kineticist is interested in the detailed mechanism by which charge transfer occurs between a solid conducting or semiconducting phase and a reactant in solution. To treat this subject it is necessary to understand:

(1) The characteristics that make electrode reactions different from ordinary homogeneous chemical reactions.

(2) What happens to the concentrations of reactant in the solution layer next to electrodes.

(3) The detailed structure of the interfacial region between the electrode and solution, in the range of about 10–100 Å, where all of the potential drop occurs.

The following discussion will touch briefly on these three points.

Electrode reactions are heterogeneous processes that involve charge transfer steps and mass transfer steps; in principle, either kind of step can be rate-determining. In some electrode reactions that have been studied actual transfer of charge seems to be the slowest step involved; a case in point is the electrodeposition of silver. Another example is to be found in the familiar hydrogen electrode:

$$2H^+(aq) + 2e^- \rightarrow H_2(g) \qquad (15\text{-}19)$$

One observed mechanism for the reduction of H^+ to molecular hydrogen is as follows:

$$H^+ + e^- + M \rightarrow H\text{---}M \qquad (15\text{-}20)$$
$$H\text{---}M + H\text{---}M \rightarrow H_2(g) + M + M \qquad (15\text{-}21)$$

where M is an adsorption site on the surface of the electrode. Either reaction may be the slow step depending on conditions. When Equation (15-20) is the slow step a dependence of rate on the nature of the electrode is expected because of the necessity of forming hydrogen-metal bonds. Experimentally, it is found, for example, that the reaction is 10^{10} times slower on a mercury electrode than on a platinum electrode, simply because of the difference in hydrogen-metal bond strengths. Here is a difference in reactivity resulting from a "modest" structural change that is essentially unparalleled in nonelectrochemical processes.

As another example of an electrode process we consider the reduction in aqueous solution of chromium(III) ion to chromium(II) ion,

$$Cr^{3+}(aq) + e^- \rightarrow Cr^{2+}(aq) \qquad (15\text{-}22)$$

and we now ask: what is the slow step? The answer turns out to be neither atom incorporation into a crystal nor bond formation. In aqueous solution both ions are octahedrally hydrated so that Equation (15-22) is more correctly written as

$$Cr(H_2O)_6^{3+} + e^- \rightarrow Cr(H_2O)_6^{2+} \quad (Slow) \qquad (15\text{-}23)$$

The rate-determining step involves concurrent thermal fluctuations of the Cr(III)—H_2O bonds in the aquo ion and addition of the electron at a propitious time when one of these fluctuations places the molecule about half-way to the equilibrium position that is demanded by the Cr(II) complex. Potential energy curves can be drawn for steps such as this one and used to predict how fast the reaction will proceed.

We now ask just what is meant by the rate of an electrode reaction? The accepted way for formulating the rate in one direction of a reaction such as that in Equation (15–23) is as follows:

$$\text{Rate}^{\rightarrow} = k^{\rightarrow}{}_h[\text{Cr}(\text{H}_2\text{O})_6^{3+}]_{x=0} \times A \tag{15–24}$$

where the subscript h means that the rate constant is a heterogeneous rate constant; this constant has units of centimeters per second. The concentration term is not the bulk concentration, but must be evaluated at the surface ($x = 0$) of the electrode. The quantity A is simply the area of the electrode. Experimentally, the rate is measured by measuring current. Forward and backward currents for processes involving transfer of n electrons (in our case $n = 1$) are formulated as

$$i^{\rightarrow} = \mathfrak{F}nk^{\rightarrow}{}_h[\text{Cr}(\text{H}_2\text{O})_6^{3+}]_{x=0} \times A \tag{15–25}$$
$$^{\leftarrow}i = \mathfrak{F}nk^{\leftarrow}{}_h[\text{Cr}(\text{H}_2\text{O})_6^{2+}]_{x=0} \times A \tag{15–26}$$

where $\mathfrak{F}$ is the Faraday number. The current which we actually observe, however, is $i^{\rightarrow} - {}^{\leftarrow}i$. When the potential of the electrode is at equilibrium, the observed current will be zero, so that $i^{\rightarrow} = {}^{\leftarrow}i = i^{\rightleftarrows}$, where $i^{\rightleftarrows}$ is called the exchange current. This quantity gives a comparative idea of how fast electrons can be exchanged; its magnitude is found to vary considerably. For the hydrogen evolution reaction on mercury electrodes [Equation (15–19)] $i^{\rightleftarrows} = 10^{-13}$ amperes cm^{-2}, while for the mercury/mercury(I) electrode reaction it is about 0.5 amperes cm^{-2}.

The potential of the electrode at which $i^{\rightarrow} = {}^{\leftarrow}i$ is that expressed by the Nernst equation (see Exercise 2, Chapter 4)

$$\mathcal{E}_{eq} = \mathcal{E}^{\circ} + \frac{RT}{n\mathfrak{F}} \ln \left(\frac{\text{Cr}(\text{H}_2\text{O})_6^{3+}}{\text{Cr}(\text{H}_2\text{O})_6^{2+}} \right)_{eq} \tag{15–27}$$

It is understood that the standard potential $\mathcal{E}^{\circ}$ is simply the potential of a cell in which the following reaction occurs:

$$\text{Cr}(\text{H}_2\text{O})_6^{3+} + \tfrac{1}{2}\text{H}_2(g) \overset{K}{\rightleftharpoons} \text{Cr}(\text{H}_2\text{O})_6^{2+} + \text{H}^+(\text{aq}) \tag{15–28}$$

where the temperature is 25°C, the pressure of the hydrogen gas is 1 atm and the activities of H^+, $Cr(H_2O)_6^{3+}$, and $Cr(H_2O)_6^{2+}$ are unity:

$$\mathcal{E}^\circ = -\frac{\Delta \tilde{G}^\circ}{n\mathfrak{F}} = \frac{RT}{n\mathfrak{F}} \ln K \qquad (15\text{–}29)$$

Substituting back into the Nernst equation we have

$$\mathcal{E}_{eq} = \frac{RT}{n\mathfrak{F}} \left[\ln K + \ln \left(\frac{Cr(H_2O)_6^{3+}}{Cr(H_2O)_6^{2+}} \right)_{eq} \right]$$

so that

$$\left(\frac{Cr(H_2O)_6^{2+}}{Cr(H_2O)_6^{3+}} \right)_{eq} = K \exp \left(-\frac{\mathcal{E}_{eq}\mathfrak{F}}{RT} \right) \qquad (15\text{–}30)$$

However, by equating expressions for the forward and backward currents [Equations (15–25) and (15–26)], we can easily show that

$$\left(\frac{Cr(H_2O)_6^{3+}}{Cr(H_2O)_6^{2+}} \right)_{eq} = \frac{\overset{\leftarrow}{k}_h}{\vec{k}_h} \qquad (15\text{–}31)$$

so that Equation (15–30) finally takes the form

$$\frac{\vec{k}_h}{\overset{\leftarrow}{k}_h} = K \exp \left(-\frac{\mathcal{E}_{eq}\mathfrak{F}}{RT} \right) \qquad (15\text{–}32)$$

It is seen that the value of the ratio of the rate constants is dependent on the potential. This exponential dependence of rate constants on potential is characteristic of an electrochemical rate.

When the system is away from equilibrium, it turns out that the individual rate constants also depend on the potential:

$$k_h = k_h^\circ \exp - \frac{\alpha n \mathfrak{F} \mathcal{E}}{RT} \qquad (15\text{–}33)$$

where k_h° is a standard rate constant and α is called the transfer coefficient, having values between zero and unity. Part of present-day theoretical electrochemistry is the a priori calculation of the transfer coefficient.

Because electrode reactions are heterogeneous it is necessary to pay attention to the metal-solution interface. An electric potential difference will appear at the boundary between two dissimilar

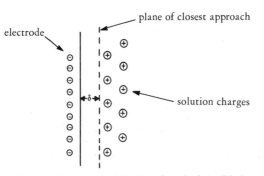

FIGURE 15–15   A model for the electrical double layer.

electrically conducting phases, and the magnitude of the potential drop depends intimately on the nature and composition of the two phases. An early model proposed by Helmholtz pictured the interface as consisting of an excess of ions or electrons on the metal and an equivalent amount of oppositely charged ions in the solution situated in the first few molecular layers away from the metal surface. Improvement is obtained if the charge on the solution side is no longer regarded as a continuous surface charge, but as a space charge having a statistical distribution. These two models have been amalgamated by Stern, who postulates that the solution charges cannot approach the metal surface charges any closer than a certain minimum distance, δ (see Figure 15–15). This "plane of closest approach" is within one or two solvent molecules of the electrode surface.

A typical value of δ might lie in the range 1–5 Å. According to Stern's theory a plot of potential as a function of distance from the metal surface would be as shown in Figure 15–16.

Two effects of the presence of the electrical double layer may be summarized quickly.

(a) The concentration of an ionic species at the plane of closest approach, which is the site of electrode reactions, is not equal to the bulk concentration, but rather to the following expression:

$$[ION]_{x=\delta} = [ION]_{\delta bulk} \exp\left(-\frac{z\mathfrak{F}\psi_\delta}{RT}\right) \qquad (15\text{–}34)$$

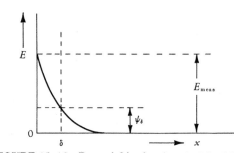

FIGURE 15–16   Potential in the electrical double layer.

where z is the charge of the ion.

(b) The potential which the ion experiences is not equal to the potential that is experimentally measured, but rather to

$$\varepsilon_{\text{actual}} = \varepsilon_{\text{meas}} - \psi_\delta \qquad (15\text{-}35)$$

Now consider a case where the rate of the charge transfer is so large that it is no longer rate-determining. In this case the current does not increase without limit but instead becomes limited by the rate at which reactant can be supplied to the electrode surface. When diffusion is the controlling mass transfer process the current obeys the relation

$$i = \frac{n\mathfrak{F}AD}{l}(C^\circ - C_{x=0}) \qquad (15\text{-}36)$$

where D is the diffusion coefficient of the reactant, C° is its bulk concentration, and l is the linear dimension of the solution layer across which the diffusion occurs. Note that the heterogeneous rate constant for the electrode reaction does not appear in Equation (15-36) because we are considering a case in which the rate of the charge transfer process does not affect the current.

The concentration of reactant at the electrode surface, $C_{x=0}$, is decreased to zero when the potential applied to the electrode is sufficient, and it follows from Equation (15-36) that further increases in applied potential can lead to no further increase in current. The current-potential behavior observed is shown in Figure (15–17).

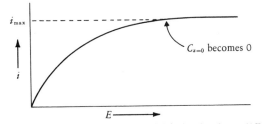

FIGURE 15-17 **Current-potential behavior for a diffu-sion-controlled electrode reaction.**

When both the reactant and product involved in the electrode reaction are stable, soluble species and the potential is adjusted so that the current is exactly one-half of the maximum current, the electrode finds itself in an environment in which the concentrations of both reactant and product are $\frac{1}{2}C°$. This means that the logarithmic term in the Nernst equation will vanish and the observed electrode potential will be the standard potential for the redox couple being studied. This provides a neat and nifty method for evaluating standard potentials—especially in cases where the product of the electrode reaction is difficult to prepare by standard chemical procedures.

Index

Acid ionization
 of acids of sulfur, selenium, tellu-
  rium, and phosphorus, 11
 of aliphatic carboxylic acids, 12
 Born-Haber cycle, 18–27
 of cinnamic acids, 16
 entropy of, 29
 estimation of ionization constant, 9
 in glacial acetic acid, 36
 and Hammett $\rho\sigma$ equation,
  15–16
 of hydrohalic acids (see
  Hydrohalic acids)
 and oxygen content, 11–12
 relation to electroreduction of
  diatomic species, 32–33
 of second-row acids, 10
 and solubility data, 17
 of substituted benzoic acids, 13
 in terms of chemical potentials,
  7–8
 in terms of pK, 8
Activation energy, 155, 172
Activity, 8

Activity coefficient, 8
 of the hydrogen ion, 10
Arrhenius, S., 67
Arrhenius equation, 70, 83, 155
Associative mechanism (see Reaction
  mechanism)
Atomic carbon
 preparation of, 161
 reactions with hydrocarbons,
  163–166
Axial substituent, 170

Basolo, F., 149
Benzene
 nitration of, 90–91
 triple point of, 6
Bernstein, R. B., 160
Beuhler, R. J., Jr., 160
Bodenstein, M., 79, 83, 156
Boltzmann law, 79, 167
Bond energy value, 100
Born, M., 18
Born-Haber cycle, 18–27
Boron
 and diborane, 101–102

Boron
  hydrolysis of boron trichloride,
    100–101
  hydrolysis of boron trifluoride and
    fluoborate anion, 97–100,
    104
  "Bridging" bonds, 101
Bromocyclohexane, dehydro-
    bromination of, 86
Brooks, P. R., 160

Cage effect, 59
Carbon
  hydrolysis of carbon tetra-
    fluoride, 103–104
  nucleophilic attack on
    acetyl chloride, 122–123
    chlorobenzene, 123
    chloroform, 111
    p-chloronitrobenzene, 123
    methyl chloride, 105
    methyl fluoride, 105
    vinyl chloride, 122–123
  reaction of p-nitrophenyl acetate
    with nucleophiles, 131
Caro's acid, decomposition of, 86
Chemical dynamics, 1, 153
Chemical energetics, as a language
    for discussing chemical
    dynamics, 2
Chemical potential
  analogy to other potential
    quantities, 4
  application to acid ionization, 7
  of electrons, 35
  expressions for, 5
  relation to pH, 14
  relations to free energy, 4
Chemical shift, 167
Chernyaev, I. I., 142
Chromium complexes (see Electro-
    chemical dynamics)

Cobalt complexes
  entering and leaving group effects,
    149–150
  evidence for dissociative mecha-
    nism, 149
  ligand substitution processes, 91,
    147–151
Coleman lamps, 42
Collision
  classical theory, 78–79, 155–156
  complexes, 57
  implicitly defined, 48
  "sticky" collisions, 157
  (see also Reaction cross section)
Complexes (see Metallic central
    ions, Cobalt complexes,
    Platinum complexes)
Computers, use of to solve dynamics
    problems, 47
Concerted mechanism (see Reaction
    mechanism)
Cross-molecular beam experiment
  with alkali metals and alkyl
    halides, 47, 154
  schematic diagram, 46
Crystal field splitting parameter,
    147
Crystal lattic energy, 25, 28
  of alkali fluorides, 29

Debye, P., 121
Decay
  of excited calcium atoms, 63
  of excited cyclopropane, 54
  of excited oxygen-alkene adducts,
    53
  fluorescence, 51
  implicitly defined, 48
  as intramolecular and/or inter-
    molecular energy transfer,
    49–50

Decay
  phosphorescence, 50
  vibrational-translational energy
    transfer, 55–56
Diborane (*see* Boron)
Dichlorocarbene, 93
Dielectric constant, 58–59
Dielectric relaxation (*see* Fast reac-
    tions)
Diethylenetriamine, 61
Diffusion-controlled reaction
  diffusion coefficient, 59, 64,
    178
  in electrochemical processes,
    178–179
  rate constants for, 60
  (*see also* Smoluchowski-Debye
    equation)
1,1-Difluorocyclohexane, conforma-
    tional interconversion, 84,
    170–171
Double layer (*see* Electrochemical
    dynamics)

Edwards equation, 121
Eigen, M., 47
Electrochemical cell, 34
Electrochemical dynamics
  and the electrical double layer,
    177
  exchange current, 175
  and rate laws, 175–176
  rate-determining charge transfer,
    174
  rate-determining mass transfer,
    174
  reduction of chromium(III) to
    chromium(II), 174–176
Electrochemical reduction
  of diatomic species, 32–33
  experimental measurement of re-
    duction potentials, 34

Electrochemical reduction
  reduction potentials for halogens,
    36
  relation of reduction potential to
    equilibrium constant, 38
Electron affinity, 19, 20, 23
  of second-row elements, 101
Elementary process, 43, 47–48
  (*see also* Collision, Decay)
Encounter, 59, 80
Entering group, 117, 133
Enthalpy
  for equilibria of halogens, 56
  of formation of alkali halides, 29
  of gas phase dissociation, 33
  invariance with temperature, 21
  lattice enthalpy, 25, 28, 29
Entropy
  for equilibria of halogens, 56
  invariance with temperature, 21
  of ionization, 29
Equatorial substituent, 170
Equilibrium constant, 3
  and free energy, 70
  and pK, 8
  and reduction potential, 38
Ethane, reaction with atomic car-
    bon, 164–165
Ethylene
  chlorination of, 86
  reaction with atomic carbon, 163
Ethylenediamine, 149
Extensive quantities, 4
Eyring, H., 80

Faraday constant, 35
Fast reactions
  methods for monitoring, 62–63
  rate constants for, 60
Finkelstein reaction, 106
Flash photolysis (*see* Fast reactions)
Fluorescence (*see* Decay)

Fluorine, mechanism for hydrolysis
    of, 112–113
Fluoronitrene, 109
Free energy, 3
    of activation, 81
    and chemical potential, 4
    for equilibria of halogens, 56
    and equilibrium constant, 70
    and pK, 9
    and reduction potential, 35
    of solvation, 20, 23–24
    a state function, 20
    usefulness of, 2
    of vaporization, 20–21
Fuel cell, 38

Gauche conformation, 168
General acid catalysis, 99
Grunwald, E., 130
Gutowsky, H. S., 84
Gyromagnetic ratio, 166

Haber, F., 18
Half-life, 76
Hammett $\rho\sigma$ equation, 15–16
Hard and soft acids and bases, 126–
    128
Heat of sublimation, 25, 102
Henry's law, 28
Herschbach, D. R., 47, 156
Hess's law, 22
"Hot reactions," 162
Hydrogen electrode, 35, 174
Hydrohalic acids
    bond dissociation energies, 36
    degree of ionization, 27
    ionization data for, 14, 36
    ionization described by a Born-
        Haber cycle, 26–27
    ionization related to reduction po-
        tentials of halogens, 36

Inner sphere complex, 133–134
Intensive quantities, 4, 65
Inversion of configuration, 113–114
Iodide-hypochlorite reaction
    mechanisms for, 72–75
    monitoring of, 66
Ionization potential, 19, 20
    of anions, 23
    of the hydrogen atom, 20, 23
    of second-row elements, 101

Johnson, S. A., 149
Jones, E. M., 160

Karplus, M., 49
Kinetic molecular theory, 62
Kistiakowsky, G. B., 62
Kramer, K. H., 160
Kwei, G. H., 156

Landau, L., 56
Lattice energy (see Enthalpy)
Lewis, W. C. McC., 78
Linear free energy relation, 84, 117

Madelung constant, 29
Mean free path, 83
Mean lifetime of a nuclear spin
    state, 171
Metallic central ions
    correlation of rates, 136
    rates of ligand substitution pro-
        cesses, 134–135
Methane, chlorination of, 90
Methyldiimide, 110
Molar refraction, 119

Neopentyl alcohol, rearrangement of,
    87
Nernst equation, 38, 175–176
Nitramide, decomposition of in
    water, 44

Nitrogen
    hydrolysis of N-chlorodimethyli-
        mine, 124
    hydrolysis of nitrogen trichloride,
        108
    hydrolysis of nitrosyl chloride,
        124
    nucleophilic attack on
        difluoramine, 108–111
        nitrogen trifluoride, 107
Norris, J. A., 156
Norrish, R. G. W., 47
Nuclear magnetic resonance spectro-
    scopy, 166–167
    conformational interconversion in
        cyclohexanes, 169–170
        (*see also* 1,1-Difluorocyclo-
        hexane)
    conformational interconversion in
        1,2-difluorotetrachloro-
        ethane, 168–169
    spin-spin splitting, 171
"Nuclear magnets," 166
Nucleophilicity parameter (*see*
    Swain-Scott equation)

Order of a reaction, 76, 82
Outer coordination sphere, 133–134
Oxygen, nucleophilic attack on
    oxygen dichloride, 112
    oxygen difluoride, 111–112

Pauling, L., 14
Pearson, R. G., 126, 149
Pelzer, H., 80
Phosphorescence (*see* Decay)
Phosphorus
    gaseous dissociation of phospho-
        rus pentachloride, 2–3
    hydrolysis of phosphorus trichlo-
        ride, 115, 125

Phosphorus
    reaction of methylisopropoxy-
        phosphoryl fluoride with
        nucleophiles, 125, 131
Photoelectric effect, 173
Pinacol, conversion to pinacolone,
    87
pK, 8
    relation to free energy, 9
    relation to pH, 9
Platinum complexes
    isolation of five-coordinate inter-
        mediates, 140
    kinetics of substitution processes,
        140–142
    ligand substitution processes, 61,
        91, 139–147
    and other square-planar com-
        plexes, 147
    steric effects, 145
    trans effect, 142–145
Polanyi, M., 154–156
Polarizability, 64, 119–121, 126
Porter, G., 47
Principle of microscopic reversibil-
    ity, 42

Raschig synthesis of hydrazine, 114
Rate constant, 50, 60, 66
Rate-determining step, 43, 68, 174
Reactants
    electrophilic and nucleophilic,
        88
    oxidant and reductant, 89
    polar and nonpolar, 89
Reaction cross section, 48
    for hard spheres, 159–160
    for the reaction of tritium with
        molecular hydrogen, 49
Reaction mechanism, 43
    chain and nonchain, 89–90

Reaction mechanism
  concerted, 138, 151
  dissociative and associative, 91,
    137–138, 150
  for iodide-hypochlorite reaction,
    72–75
Reactions
  addition reactions, 86
  elimination reactions, 86
  rearrangements, 86–87
  redox reactions, 87
  substitution reactions, 85
Reagent, 85
Rhodium complexes, reaction with
  nucleophiles, 149

Smoluchowski-Debye equation, 59
Solvation, 57
  electrostatic model for, 58
Solvolysis, 76, 130
Specific acid catalysis, 99
Spectrophone (see Fast reactions)
Spectroscopy
  infrared, 21
  nuclear magnetic resonance (see
    Nuclear magnetic resonance
    spectroscopy)
  ultraviolet, 23–24, 66
Spin-spin splitting, 171
Standard state, 5
Steady-state hypothesis, 76, 151
Stern, O., 177
Substrate, 85
Sullivan, J. H., 156

Swain-Scott equation, 119

Teller, E., 56
Temperature jump method (see Fast
    reactions)
Tetramethylsilane, 167
Thermal reactions, 162
Thermodynamics
  as language of chemical energet-
    ics, 2
  as supplier of boundary conditions
    on chemical reactions, 41
Thionyl chloride, 114
Threshold energy, 49
Trans conformation, 168
Trans effect (see Platinum com-
    plexes)
Transfer coefficient, 176
Transition state theory, 80–82
Transmission coefficient κ, 82
Trautz, M., 78

Ultrasonics (see Fast reactions)

Volta effect, 173
Volt-coulomb, 35
von Hartel, H., 154–156
von Helmholtz, H. L. F., 177

Y-Values of Winstein and Grun-
    wald, 130–131

Werner, A., 142
Wigner, E., 80
Winstein, S., 130